P9-CJC-703

Literature & Thought

Times of Change
Vietnam and the 60s

Perfection Learning

EDITORIAL DIRECTOR   Julie A. Schumacher

SENIOR EDITOR   Terry Ofner

EDITOR   Sherrie Voss Matthews

REVIEWERS   Laurie Bauer

DESIGN AND PHOTO RESEARCH   William Seabright and Associates, Wilmette, Illinois

COVER ART   THE VIETNAM WAR 1984 Kenneth Willhite

ACKNOWLEDGMENTS

Preface from *Portrait of a Tragedy: America and the Vietnam War,* by James A. Warren. Lothrop, Lee & Shepard Books, New York. Copyright 1990.

The Times They Are A-Changin' - Copyright © 1963, 1964 by Warner Bros. Music, Copyright renewed 1990 by Special Rider Music. All rights reserved. International copyright secured. Reprinted by permission.

"The Swinging Sixties", from *Time Capsule: Short Stories About Teenagers Throughout the Twentieth Century* by Donald R. Gallo, copyright © 1999 by Donald R. Gallo. Used by permission of Dell Publishing, a division of Random House, Inc.

"Ballad of the Green Berets" Eastaboga Music/Barry Sadler and Robin Moore. Reprinted by permission.

"History" by Thuong Vuong-Riddick reprinted by permission from *Two Shores: Deux Rives.* Vancouver: Ronsdale Press, 1995.

"The Gulf of Tonkin Resolution May Have Been The Gulf Between Truth And Fiction" from *The Book of Lies: Histories Greatest Fakes, Frauds, Schemes and Scams* by M. Hirsh Goldberg. William Morrow and Company, Inc., New York. 1990.

"Jack Smith" from *The Soldiers' Story: Vietnam in their own words* by Ron Steinman. TV Books, LLC, New York. 1999.

"On the Rainy River" from *The Things They Carried.* Copyright © 1990 by Tim O'Brien. Reprinted by permission of Houghton Mifflin Co./Seymour Lawrence. All rights reserved. CONTINUED ON PAGE 143

Copyright © 2001 by Perfection Learning Corporation
1000 North Second Avenue
P.O. Box 500, Logan, Iowa 51546-0500
Tel: 1-800-831-4190 • Fax: 1-712-644-2392

All rights reserved. No part of this book may be used or reproduced in any manner whatsoever without written permission from the publisher. Printed in the United States of America

Paperback ISBN: 0-7891-5268-1

Cover Craft ® ISBN: 0-7891-9688-8

1 2 3 4 5 6 DR 05 04 03 02 01 00

What effect did the decade of the 60s have on the United States?

The question above is the *essential question* that you will consider as you read this book. The literature, activities, and organization of the book will lead you to think critically about this question and to develop a deeper understanding of America's involvement in Vietnam and the decade of the 60s.

To help you shape your answer to the broad essential question, you will read and respond to four sections, or clusters. Each cluster addresses a specific question and thinking skill.

CLUSTER ONE What were the roots of the conflict? **SUMMARIZE**

CLUSTER TWO What was the war experience? **ANALYZE**

CLUSTER THREE What was happenning back home? **GENERALIZE**

CLUSTER FOUR Thinking on your own **SYNTHESIZE**

Notice that the final cluster asks you to think independently about your answer to the essential question—*What effect did the decade of the 60s have on the United States?*

TIMES OF CHANGE

Vietnam and the 60s

The Times They Are A-Changin'

Come gather 'round people wherever you roam
And admit that the waters around you have grown
And accept it that soon you'll be drenched to the bone.
If your time to you is worth savin'
Then you'd better start swimmin' or you'll sink like a stone

For the times, they are a-changin'.

Come writers and critics who prophesize with your pen
And keep you eyes wide, the chance won't come again
And don't speak too soon, for the wheel's still in spin
And there's no tellin' who that it's namin'
For the loser now will be later to win

For the times, they are a-changin'.

Come senators, congressmen, please heed the call
Don't stand in the doorway, don't block the hall
For he that gets hurt will be he who has stalled
There's a battle outside and it's ragin'
It'll soon shake your windows and rattle your walls

For the times, they are a-changin'.

Come mothers and fathers throughout the land
And don't criticize what you can't understand
Your sons and your daughters are beyond your command
Your old road is rapidly agin'
Please get out of the new one if you can't lend a hand

For the times, they are a-changin'.

The line, it is drawn, the curse, it is cast
The slow one now will later be fast
And the present now will later be past
The order is rapidly fadin'
And the first one now will later be last

For the times, they are a-changin'.

BOB DYLAN

TABLE OF CONTENTS

PROLOGUE   THE TIMES THEY ARE A-CHANGIN' BY BOB DYLAN   4

CREATING CONTEXT   9

The Swinging Sixties · A Dubious Crusade · Map of Southeast Asia ·
Timeline · Concept Vocabulary

CLUSTER ONE   What Were the Roots of the Conflict?   16

Thinking Skill   SUMMARIZING

FLASHBACK

Ballad of the Green Berets
SGT. BARRY SADLER   song lyrics   16

History
THUONG VUONG-RIDDICK   poem   18

**The Gulf of Tonkin Resolution May Have
Been the Gulf Between Truth and Fiction**
M. HIRSH GOLDBERG   article   20

Jack Smith
RON STEINMAN   oral history   23

On the Rainy River
TIM O'BRIEN   short story   33

RESPONDING TO CLUSTER ONE

Writing Activity   A POETIC SUMMARY   48

CLUSTER TWO   What Was the War Experience?   49

Thinking Skill   ANALYZING

FLASHBACK

I-Feel-Like-I'm-Fixin'-To-Die Rag
JOE McDONALD   song lyrics   50

Hippies
ALEX FORMAN   memoir   53

Village
ESTELA PORTILLO   short story   57

Farmer Nguyen
W. D. EHRHART   poem   64

The Massacre at My Lai
HUGH THOMPSON   essay   67

A Nun in Ninh Hoa
JAN BERRY   poem   69

A Piece of My Heart
ANNE SIMON AUGER
AS TOLD TO KEITH WALKER   oral history   71

RESPONDING TO CLUSTER TWO

Writing Activity SPINNING THE NEWS   **78**

CLUSTER THREE **What Was Happening Back Home?**   **79**

Thinking Skill GENERALIZING

FLASHBACK

**San Francisco (Be Sure to Wear
Some Flowers in Your Hair)**
JOHN PHILLIPS   song lyrics   80

Law and Order Chicago Style
DONALD KAUL   essay   82

Like a Rolling Stone
BEN FONG-TORRES   memoir   85

Woodstock Nation
MARC ARONSON   essay   89

Woodstock: The Oral History
IRWIN UNGER   interviews   91

**State of Emergency at
"The People's Republic of Berkeley"**
TOM HAYDEN   memoir   95

Cambodia
PRESIDENT RICHARD M. NIXON   speech   98

The Kent State Tragedy
ROGER BARR   article   101

Born on the Fourth of July
from *Born on the Fourth of July*   autobiography
RON KOVIC   103

RESPONDING TO CLUSTER THREE
Writing Activity   DUELING LETTERS TO THE EDITOR   **108**

CLUSTER FOUR   Thinking on Your Own   **109**

Thinking Skill   SYNTHESIZING

FLASHBACK
Where Have All the Flowers Gone?
PETE SEEGER   song lyrics   110

Epilogue
PHILIP CAPUTO   autobiography   112

A President's Pain
PRESIDENT GERALD R. FORD   vignette   117

The Summer of Vietnam
BARBARA RENAUD GONZÁLEZ   essay   118

Stop the Sun
GARY PAULSEN   short story   121

To Heal a Nation
JOEL L. SWERDLOW   article   129

RESPONDING TO CLUSTER FOUR   **142**

The Swinging Sixties

DONALD R. GALLO

The "Swinging Sixties" were characterized by long hair, go-go boots, miniskirts, bell-bottom pants, psychedelic art, and sex, drugs and rock and roll, led by such groups as the Beatles, the Rolling Stones, and the Supremes. "Flower children" wearing peace symbols bloomed in communes across the United States as well as in Europe.

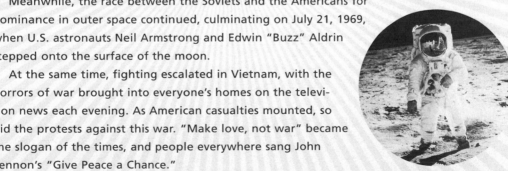

More significantly, the struggle for racial equality begun in the late fifties continued with demonstrations, voter registration drives, race riots, the murders of civil rights activists as well as innocent children, and a march through Washington, D.C., highlighted by Martin Luther King, Jr.'s "I have a dream" speech and the singing of "We Shall Overcome."

Before the decade was over, Reverend King had been assassinated, as had been Black Muslim leader Malcom X, President John F. Kennedy, and his brother Bobby Kennedy.

Meanwhile, the race between the Soviets and the Americans for dominance in outer space continued, culminating on July 21, 1969, when U.S. astronauts Neil Armstrong and Edwin "Buzz" Aldrin stepped onto the surface of the moon.

At the same time, fighting escalated in Vietnam, with the horrors of war brought into everyone's homes on the television news each evening. As American casualties mounted, so did the protests against this war. "Make love, not war" became the slogan of the times, and people everywhere sang John Lennon's "Give Peace a Chance."

A Dubious Crusade

JAMES A. WARREN

The Vietnam War, or the Second Indochina War, as it is sometimes called, was the longest and most controversial conflict in American history. Because the government of the United States never officially called the conflict in Vietnam a war, it's hard to say just when it began. The first official American deaths in Vietnam occurred in 1959. Although very few Americans died in the jungles of Southeast Asia until 1965, when the first combat units were sent there, the U.S. government supplied the French with money and equipment to fight the Vietnamese communists in their war, which began in 1946, and continued to support anticommunists in Vietnam up to 1975.

All wars are complex, brutal affairs that test the endurance of soldier and ordinary citizen alike. The Vietnam War, in which the United States, its allies, and South Vietnam fought against rebels within South Vietnam called the Vietcong and communists from North Vietnam, tested the endurance and the understanding of the American people in ways that other wars have not.

As an episode of military history, Vietnam is really just beginning to be explored, and its importance goes far beyond military history. The American experience in Vietnam provides us with a wealth of clues and insights about modern American history and American values. When President John F. Kennedy was laying the groundwork for direct American intervention in Vietnam in the early 1960s, the United States had reached the height of its power and self-confidence. We were the unchallenged leaders of the free world. There was a belief among the nation's leaders that the United States was invincible, that it had not only the political and military might to do what it wanted where it wanted, but also the moral authority to do so.

In 1975, Americans watched on television the humiliating evacuation of Saigon, the capital city of South Vietnam. The surrender of the city to the communists ended a terrible era in our history—an era that changed us. America was an entirely different nation than it had been back in the early 1960s. We were no longer so sure of our path, no longer confident that we had the answers to all the important questions.

The war had come close to tearing the nation apart. The American public no longer trusted its government. The armed forces of the nation had become demoralized and fragmented. The soul and conscience of the nation had been deeply wounded. And more than 57,000 men had sacrificed their lives in what is now thought to be a dubious crusade.

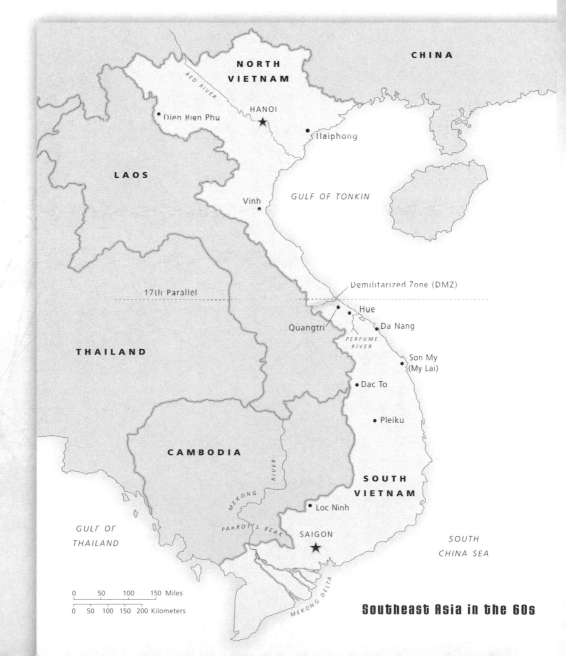

Southeast Asia in the 60s

On the Home Front

1960

- Four African Americans stage a sit-in at Woolworth's to desegregate the lunch counter.

1962

- U.S. President Kennedy demands Russian nuclear missiles be removed from Cuba during the Cuban Missile Crisis. The United States and Russia come close to nuclear war.

1963

- Martin Luther King, Jr., gives "I have a dream" speech at the March on Washington.
- South Vietnamese President Ngo Dihn Diem assassinated.
- U.S. President John F. Kennedy assassinated.

1964

- U.S. President Lyndon Johnson launches his "Great Society"— a plan to end poverty and improve the standard of living for all Americans.

1965

- Watts riots in Los Angeles.
- Draft-card burning made illegal.
- A London boutique owner displays the first miniskirt.

1950

- The United States begins to subsidize the French war in Vietnam as an attempt to "contain" Communism. China supplies weapons to the Vietminh.
- U.S. military advisors arrive in Saigon, the capital of South Vietnam.

1954

- The French are defeated at Dien Bien Phu.
- The Geneva Conference on Indochina declares a demilitarized zone at the 17th parallel between North and South Vietnam.
- U.S. President Dwight Eisenhower pledges to support the South Vietnamese government and military forces.

1955

- The Republic of Vietnam (South Vietnam) is organized as an independent nation.

1959

- American Lt. Col. A. Peter Dewey is the first military casualty in Vietnam when he is shot by a sniper on the way to the airport.

1960

- The National Liberation Front (NLF or Vietcong) is founded in South Vietnam to oppose the government.

1961

- U.S. President John F. Kennedy begins buildup of American military forces in Vietnam.

1964

- Gulf of Tonkin incident—North Vietnamese torpedo boats allegedly attack the U.S. destroyer *Maddox*.
- U.S. Congress approves the Gulf of Tonkin resolution. President Johnson requests permission to use "any means necessary" to repel further attacks. The resolution opens the door for Johnson to send additional troops to Vietnam.

1965

- First U.S. combat troops arrive in South Vietnam.

In the War Zone

1966

- Huey P. Newton and Bobby Seale found the Black Panther Party in California.

1967

- Three astronauts die in a fire during training exercises for *Apollo I.*
- First Human Be-In celebrated; 20,000 hippies converge on Golden Gate Park in San Francisco. The summer of 1967 becomes the "Summer of Love" as hippies commune in the Haight-Ashbury district of San Francisco.
- Muhammed Ali banned from professional boxing after he refuses to be inducted into the U.S. Army on religious grounds.
- 40,000 people demonstrate against the Vietnam War in Washington, D.C.

1968

- Martin Luther King, Jr., assassinated in Memphis, Tennessee.
- Democratic presidential candidate Robert F. Kennedy assassinated.
- Yippies and war protesters riot outside the Democratic National Convention in Chicago.
- President Johnson announces that he will not run for re-election.

1969

- *Apollo XI* lands on the moon; Neil Armstrong is the first man to step on the moon.
- Woodstock Music Festival takes place in upstate New York.
- 250,000 people demonstrate against the Vietnam War in Washington, D.C.

1970

- U.S. National Guardsmen kill four students at Kent State University in Ohio.
- More than 100 colleges closed due to student riots over the deaths at Kent State.

1973

- Nixon inaugurated for second term as U.S. president.
- Watergate scandal breaks in the *Washington Post*. Investigation reveals that men were hired to spy on the Democratic National Headquarters at the Watergate Hotel in Washington, D.C.

1974

- President Nixon resigns because of the Watergate scandal.

1968

- Battle of Khe Sanh begins.
- Tet Offensive
- My Lai Massacre
- U.S. President Johnson offers to negotiate with North Vietnam for peace, and announces that he will not run for re-election.

1969

- Paris Peace Talks begin.
- U.S. President Richard Nixon announces the first troop withdrawals.
- Ho Chi Minh dies.

1970

- U.S. and South Vietnam armies invade Cambodia to cut North Vietnamese supply line.

1971

- Laos invaded.
- The *Washington Post* begins publishing the Pentagon Papers, which prove the government knew the war in Vietnam was unwinable.

1973

- United States and North Vietnam sign Paris Peace Accords. U.S. military draft ends.
- Last U.S. troops leave Vietnam.
- American POWs come home.
- North Vietnam releases the last 591 acknowledged American POWs.

1975

- Last Americans evacuated out of Saigon. Last American combat death.
- North Vietnamese forces take over Saigon.
- South Vietnam surrenders. The country is reunified under Communist control.

CONCEPT VOCABULARY

You will find the following terms and definitions useful as you read and discuss the selections in this book.

ARVN Army of the Republic of Vietnam (South Vietnam)

Cold War the era of rivalry and mistrust between the capitalist United States (with western European alies) and the Communist United Socialist Soviet Republic (Russia and its satellite states) from 1945 until 1989

conscientious objector a person who refuses to enter the military or bear arms on moral or religious grounds

containment the United States' policy of preventing the spread of Communism during the Cold War

credibility gap the distrust arising from the differences in government reports versus the media's reports

demilitarized zone area prohibited from being used for military purposes

domino theory belief that if one country in a region fell to Communism all other countries in the area would fall like a row of dominoes

draft required enrollment into the military

flower children young people who celebrated peace and love during the 1960s

generation gap the intense disagreement between young people and older generations during the era of the 1960s

Geneva Accords the 1954 agreement that allowed the temporary division of Vietnam into the Communist North and democratic South. It called for national elections to be held at a later date

hippie a young person who rejects established society and advocates nonviolence

missing in action (MIA) a soldier lost after a military maneuver

napalm a gasoline-aluminum jelly mix used in weapons that causes prolonged burning

prisoner of war (POW) a soldier captured by the opposing army

Vietcong (VC) guerrilla member of the Vietnamese Communist movement

Vietminh member of the Vietnamese Communist movement from 1941–1951

the Wall slang for the U.S. Vietnam Veterans' Memorial in Washington, D.C.

yippies the Youth International Party; a group dedicated to protesting the Vietnam War and the American economic and political systems

CLUSTER ONE

What Were the Roots of the Conflict?
Thinking Skill SUMMARIZING

Ballad of the Green Berets

STAFF SERGEANT BARRY SADLER

Fighting soldiers from the sky,
Fearless men who jump and die.
Men who mean just what they say
The fearless men of the Green Beret.

Silver wings upon their chest,
These are men, America's best.
One hundred men will test today
Only three win the Green Beret.

Trained to fight for freedom's land,
Trained in combat, hand to hand.
They will die for a better day
These brave men of the Green Beret.

Back at home a young wife waits,
Her Green Beret has met his fate.
He has died so that she may live
Leaving her this last request,

Put silver wings on my son's chest.
Make him one of America's best.
One hundred men will test that day,
And only three will win the Green Beret.

History

THUONG VUONG-RIDDICK

From China, the Yuen people traveled south, and killed
the Thai, the Khmers, the Mongs and the Chams from the
kingdom of Funan. As a result of their "Marching towards
the South," the Yuen became independent, the Viet.

Then for ten centuries the Chinese waged war and killed
the Vietnamese and called Vietnam, Annam, which means
"The Pacified South."

The French killed the Vietnamese and
occupied the country for a century.
The Vietnamese who fought the French
were called Vietminh.
The French and Vietnamese killed
the Vietminh (secretly helped by the Americans.)

The Japanese killed the French.
The Japanese allied with the French killed
the Chinese and the Vietminh.
The Japanese helped the Vietnamese to proclaim
the Independence of Vietnam.
The Japanese killed the French and were defeated.
The Americans helped the Vietminh to become
the Democratic Republic of Vietnam.
The French and their allies, the British,
killed the Vietminh.
The French equipped by the Americans lost to
the Vietminh, equipped by the Chinese.
The Americans took the place of the French.
The Vietminh were called the Vietcong.

The Vietcong armed by China and the U.S.S.R.
killed the Vietnamese and the Americans.
The Vietcong prevailed.

People fled overseas.

The Gulf of Tonkin Resolution

May Have Been the Gulf Between Truth and Fiction

M. HIRSH GOLDBERG

President Lyndon Johnson reviews the troops.

The incident that marked the beginning of America's intensive involvement in the Vietnam War has always been enshrouded in controversy.

In the summer of 1964, a U.S. Navy destroyer, the *Maddox*, on routine patrol in the Gulf of Tonkin southeast of Hanoi, was said to have been attacked suddenly and without provocation by North Vietnamese PT boats. Although the *Maddox* was not damaged, other attacks were said to have been made on U.S. destroyers. President Lyndon Johnson immediately went before Congress and urged that he be given congressional approval to defend United States interests in the area. He got it, in what has been called the Gulf of Tonkin Resolution (it passed 416–0 in the

House and 88–2 in the Senate). Shortly thereafter, although he would promise in his campaign for the presidency that year against Senator Barry Goldwater not to send American boys into battle, Lyndon Johnson ordered the beginning of what became a massive buildup of men and materials in Vietnam.

Subsequently, after the patriotic fervor died down, the scenario that led to the Resolution—the firing on a United States ship—became suspect. Many now say that it was either an incident Johnson magnified to enlist congressional support for his plan to send United States troops to fight the Viet Cong or the episode was contrived and there had been no shelling or other act of aggression against the United States that day in the Gulf of Tonkin.

An opponent of the war and a critic of Lyndon Johnson was Senator J. William Fulbright (D.-Ark.), then head of the Senate Foreign Relations Committee. He always raised the possibility that Congress had been steamrollered into supporting the Gulf of Tonkin Resolution, thereby paving the way for the Vietnam War. In the motion picture documentary *Hearts and Minds*, a winner of an Academy Award for its look at the Vietnam War, Fulbright is interviewed about the Resolution and comes close to calling Johnson a liar:

"We always hesitate in public to use the dirty word *lie*, but a lie is a lie. It is a misrepresentation of fact. It is supposed to be a criminal act if it's done under oath.

"Mr. Johnson didn't say it under oath. He just said it. We don't usually have the president under oath."

But the deed was done. The Gulf of Tonkin Resolution opened the doors to what eventually became ten years of bitter fighting (one might almost say bitter fighting both abroad and at home) in which 55,000 Americans lost their lives in one of the most protracted wars the United States has ever waged.

And yet, ironically, it was not officially a war. Only Congress can declare war, and in the case of Vietnam, Congress never did. The closest it came was the Gulf of Tonkin Resolution—which unknowingly for Congress at the time—may very well have been based upon a lie. ॐ

Jack Smith

RON STEINMAN

I flunked out of college and then I was thrown out of the house. I thought I needed a two-year vacation from the real world. My draft board told me that before I could work my way back to college, I would be drafted. So why not volunteer for the army? I thought that was a good idea. I was a bit lost, like a lot of kids my age. I was nineteen years old. I wasn't ready for college life yet, and I needed a little adventure in my life. I needed to get away for a while and grow up. A lot of kids find themselves in that position. And in 1964, joining the army seemed like a pretty good idea. The war hadn't heated up yet. People didn't associate joining the army with going to Vietnam and fighting. There really wasn't much fighting in Vietnam. It wasn't a hot issue. This was at a time when everybody, basically, joined the army. It was a common thing to do. People got drafted. It was a place where a lot of young men went to grow up before really going into life, going back to college and so forth.

I signed up for the Special Forces[1] because I had a romantic notion about the army and war and that sort of thing. I wanted to have an adventure for a few years. Through various twists and turns, and the military bureaucracy, I ended up in the infantry. We spent most of our time cleaning our rifles, going on war maneuvers, war games, getting into trouble, very boring barracks duty. Then all of a sudden, one day we were told that all the short-timers were going to be let out of the army. People who had longer time to serve would be merged with an experimental unit called the 11th Air Assault. We knew that they were experimenting

1 **Special Forces:** a branch of the Army trained for guerrilla warfare

with helicopters. We were given M-16s. We were given helicopter training. Then one day in July we listened to Lyndon Johnson give a speech when he announced that he was sending us, the 1st Cavalry Division over to Vietnam and that he was, in effect, declaring war on North Vietnam without really declaring war on North Vietnam. That's when it hit us that we were going into combat. You've got to understand, we were eighteen, nineteen, twenty years old. Very young. There hadn't been any Vietnam coverage on television. There hadn't been a war since Korea. None of us had a clue what war was about, even among the noncommissioned officers, the sergeants in my company. Only two or three of them had any combat experience. None of the officers did. We were green, green, green—which is one of the reasons why we got into trouble.

We came over on a troop ship. The night before we hit land, we passed through the Seventh Fleet at about four in the morning. We were all standing on deck with all our combat gear on ready for a combat assault on the beaches of Qui Nhon. We saw all around us the shapes of aircraft carriers, battleships, cruisers. And as the dawn broke, we saw wave after wave of aircraft taking off, going over our heads and going inland. In the darkness that still hovered over the hills that we could see in front of us, we saw bomb bursts. We heard the thud of bombs and artillery shells. Then we saw waves and waves of helicopters flying over our heads from the aircraft carriers, carrying more bombs and rockets. Then, in the dawn, we saw the beach in front of us and we said, "My God . . . this is war."

We landed on a beach, in full gear, into the surf, jumping off the ships. And we found a bunch of half-naked children, sucking their thumbs, dragging their dolls in the sand and looking at us. We were put on board helicopters or trucks and we were taken down Route 19 into the Central Highlands to An Khe, our base camp. We began with machetes and bayonets and pocket knives to carve out a base camp, chopping down all the shrubbery.

Once, just before Ia Drang, we went out on an operation. We were herded into two-and-a-half-ton trucks. As we were driving along the road, here came a convoy of trucks going in the opposite direction. They were carrying boxes of body bags. Crates of body bags. I brought this to the attention of a couple of guys standing next to me and we stared at the trucks passing by. We were going out, and the body bags were coming in, and they were for us. Nobody said a word. We all just stood in the back of the truck, rattling down the road, staring at the body bags. That was a really chill feeling. That's what combat is all about.

We had been walking through the jungle, looking for VC who were never there. Not finding anything. For two months. A couple of operations where we turned up a couple of booby traps and a pig and a few things like that. That's all. No real fighting. We had fewer combat-seasoned NCOs.[2] We had more goof-offs as privates. We weren't as well-trained—that we were sort of a parade ground outfit, a bit of a sham. That was the real feeling the men had of the battalion. I don't know how really justified it was, but that was the feeling we had. I think we were prepared as any unit's going to get prepared for combat. Nothing prepares you for combat. The best way to prepare a company for combat is to line the company up against a wall and fire a machine gun at them for about ten seconds. And tell the survivors, "You're now combat-trained." That's not pleasant, but that's what combat's like.

We walked in and we got into Landing Zone X-Ray on the third day of the battle there. It was just about over. We were goggle eyes at what we saw. I had never seen men as filthy as that. They didn't seem to be wearing clothing. Their clothing was so covered with dirt, they looked like they were part of the dirt because they had been living in the dirt, living in foxholes for three days. They all had these thousand-eye stares that people talk about. The stare of someone who is nineteen years old but going on fifty, who has seen combat and been killing people and seen his friends killed under continuous bombardment, artillery and napalm, day in, day out. Stacks of dead bodies, stacks of wounded, equipment around the landing zone. And the one thing that sticks in my mind, there were bullets whizzing over the landing zone, humming like bees. The only person standing was this colonel. He was standing in the middle of the landing zone directing traffic like a cop. We were crouched down. It was Hal Moore. That was the first guy I saw in the landing zone. Made a very vivid impression on me.

I didn't know enough to be scared. The thing about a bullet is, you can't see them. All you can do is hear them. And until you connect the sound of a bullet with someone dying, you don't have enough sense to duck. That's actually what kills most people in the early stages of combat. They hear a shot, they stick their head up, and they get killed. Even though there were some minor attacks that day and probes, we really thought it was a bit of a game. Until you've actually shot somebody or been shot yourself, it doesn't really sink in. It was beginning to sink in.

2 **NCOs:** non-commissioned officers

When I heard those bullets coming at me, I knew this was real combat. I knew those bullets could kill me. I kept my head down. I said, "Oh, my God. This is real." When the company commander said we were supposed to sit for the night, I dug a foxhole as deep as I could. The ground was as hard as gravel, so you could only dig it about six inches to a foot. Just kept my head down and hoped for the best.

The next day we walked to Landing Zone Albany for what we thought was extraction, being lifted out by helicopter. We were out for a Sunday stroll in the woods. We were strolling along, and we were a little apprehensive because we knew there had been this huge battle. We'd seen the bodies. Leaving the landing zone, you walk on bodies a hundred feet outside the dry creek bed and the foxholes. We knew there were a lot of enemy units around and some of us were a little apprehensive about walking in such a casual fashion. But we did, and a number of us remarked on it. "Shouldn't we have guards out?" And, "There are probably bad guys around here. I hope we don't get ambushed. I hope they (meaning our commanding officers) know what they are doing." In retrospect, knowing what I know now, our walk was a big mistake.

A couple of hours maybe to Landing Zone Albany, we were in an area where the brush was denser elephant grass, chest-high, waist-high, razor grass. In scrub jungle, trees here and there, all around us. Not dense forest but very light forest. You could see the sky. The head of the column broke into the landing zone. A battalion of green troops stumbling around in the jungle the day after the biggest battle of the war against an entire North Vietnamese division, right next to the main infiltration route for them in their territory without any artillery or air cover, is just nuts. Without spraying the trees, recon by fire,[3] without having guards out on the side. It's crazy. I don't know why we were walking through the jungle. I don't know why we were walking that way. It was clearly a mistake. We were green. It wasn't just the privates who were green. Everybody was green. Our captains were green. Our lieutenants were green. Our battalion commanders were green. The whole division was green. And they showed it. We walked right into a big time ambush.

The troops arrived at Landing Zone Albany and waited while their officers interrogated two captured North Vietnamese soldiers.

We just dropped down on our packs on the ground and opened our shirts and lit cigarettes and drank water. And we waited. And we waited.

3 **recon by fire:** reconnaissance, or looking for the enemy, using gunfire to clear the way

We had no leaders. No more than fifty yards away, an entire North Vietnamese battalion were setting up their ambush quietly behind ant hills. They were tying themselves up in trees while we were sitting there smoking. Our company commanders were having a conference up at the front.

Suddenly the North Vietnamese ambush the unprotected, unsuspecting troops.

I was in a half crouch saying what is this firing that's going on all around me. I turned to the lieutenant next to me—enlisted men always make fun of officers in the barracks but when it comes to combat you always look to the officer for guidance because enlisted men become paralyzed. They fire the guns but they have to be told what to do. The first two platoons of my company just fell down like you take a scythe and cut grass. No noise. Just the rattle of machine guns. These guys were twenty feet away, popping up behind ant hills, spraying us. Dozens and dozens of men with machine guns and submachine guns suddenly popped out of the ground and started spraying us. We were running toward them and I fell on the grass and began to bandage my friends up. The only time I fired my rifle, I was so confused. In combat time stops. You have no idea what you're doing. I looked up in the grass and I saw right in front of my face and right above our heads the muzzle of a machine gun firing through the elephant grass. The firing was so loud I hadn't noticed it. I took my rifle, put it on full automatic, and stuck it through the elephant grass to where I thought the gunner's head would be, and squeezed the trigger and put a magazine into this guy's head and blew his head off. After the battle I was told that right by there was a guy with no head. Probably a nineteen-year-old draftee from the Hanoi Haiphong triangle. A city kid. Probably somebody just like me. I must have been about the only man in the first two platoons who wasn't dead or wounded in the first five minutes. It was the luck of the draw.

There was an older guy who had been in World War II, in Korea. He was dying from a chest wound, lying on his back and I was comforting him and bandaging him up. I heard North Vietnamese coming. I pretended to lie dead. They swept into our clearing on the crouch, a squad of them, maybe five or six guys. They had several light machine guns with them. They saw us. They jumped down right on top of us and used us as sandbags as they set up their machine guns and they started to fire their machine guns. I had a guy lying on top of me. We all played dead. I was covered with so much blood, my friend's blood, that I looked wounded or dead. I just lay still. And I willed myself to stop breathing and not to move. But I could not control myself from shaking. I was so frightened I couldn't stop it. The only thing that saved me was the fact that the guy lying on top of me was shaking even more than I was. Combat is terrifying so he didn't notice that I was shaking, too, and that I was alive. The hot shell casings were going down inside my shirt and burning me. My friends were firing grenades at these guys. I was on the verge of going insane from fear. I said to myself, if I stand up and say, "Guys, don't shoot," the North Vietnamese will kill me. If I lie here, my guys will hit me. No sooner had I thought that, than I felt these huge explosions all around me, and a barrage of rifle grenades landed right in our clearing. One killed the sergeant whose shoulder I was sitting on. And the other grenade landed on top of the guy on top of me and blew him to bits and wounded me on my left side. I was the only person left alive in that little clearing among the Vietnamese and Americans. I bandaged myself, crawled through the grass to where the mortar platoon had been. By then they were just a pile of very badly wounded men. That's where I stayed the rest of the afternoon and night.

Later they started to mortar us. A mortar went off behind me, almost between my legs and got me in the right leg. I actually severed a vein and I had to put a tourniquet on my right leg. It was dusk. I was in a haze of pain and shock but I was alive. I remember pinching myself and saying, "I am alive." The men around me were just groaning. Moaning, semi-conscious. I was sort of semi-conscious. I was saying to myself, "My God, I'm alive." To celebrate that, I wanted a cigarette. I pulled out a cigarette and both ends were bloody so I tore them off. I said, "You know, they'll see the smoke and kill me." I said, "I don't give a damn. I want a cigarette," so I lit the damn thing and I sat there and took two or three drags and it felt heavenly. I can't explain why one does crazy things. I was very lucky.

I heard the Skyraiders[4] coming over the trees and I said, "Oh God, don't drop bombs or napalm on us, please. We're too mixed up, the North Vietnamese and Americans. You'll kill Americans." I saw stuff, big stuff coming down through the trees and I went, "Oh, no." Then in front of me there were a whole bunch of explosions and then there was a blast of heat like you open an oven door and the grass on top of me curled over from the heat. I heard people screaming and I heard them hollering

---

4 **Skyraiders:** military aircraft used for airborne attacks

in English, not just Vietnamese. Some of it got some Americans and it was right next to my position. That's really frightening. Napalm is really, really scary. It's a very effective weapon, though.

They were going through the elephant grass in the afternoon and at night killing the wounded. You would hear them walking through the grass talking Vietnamese. Then you would hear a lot of loud talking and then you would hear a GI's voice, "No, no. Don't shoot me." Then you would hear bang, bang, bang. They were going around killing the wounded systematically.

The wounded mortar platoon leader calls artillery in on their position, eventually causing the North Vietnamese troops to retreat.

That's what kept us all alive. Otherwise we all would have been killed. I think I passed out for a while. When I woke up it was getting to be daylight. The ground was littered with smashed equipment. Everything had been ripped and torn by bullets. The elephant grass was pressed down, squashed, cut down by bullets and fragments. The grass and ground were literally covered with blood. Everywhere you put your hand was sticky with blood and the place smelled of gunpowder, blood, and urine. There were North Vietnamese snipers hanging out of the trees, dead on ropes. They'd tied themselves up. In front of me was a dead man staring up at the sky. He had dirt on his eyeballs, and one of his legs was gone. There were body parts lying all around me. The dead were stacked on top of each other, sometimes with their hands around each other's throats. It looked like the devil's butcher shop. I've never seen anything like that in my life, and I hope I never, never ever do again.

When they came to get us out, our guys were walking toward us and I had a radio by then. I heard this burst of fire and I said, "Don't shoot, don't shoot." They said over the radio, "We're killing North Vietnamese wounded." And I said, "Don't kill the wounded, please. Don't kill the wounded." I didn't want any more killing. They said, "No, they did it to us. They hurt us. We're going to hurt them back." So the people who came to rescue me as they walked through the woods were killing the North Vietnamese wounded. That was in the heat of battle, I would maintain. I would maintain that what the North Vietnamese did to us was systematic. But at the time it didn't seem like much of a distinction.

I was angry at anybody who had anything to do with that battle. All my friends died there. I was even angry at the state of being human that the weakness of the flesh would succumb to shrapnel and bullets. I said, "How weak and flimsy we are that we all get killed like that." I became

CLASS OF '67 1984 Charlie Shobe The National Vietnam Veterans Art Museum

very cynical. Not only angry. But I became misanthropic.[5] One day I woke up a few years later and I saw life as it really is. Life is pretty good. The world is a pretty good, warm place. People make mistakes. It happens in other wars. There's nothing I can do about it. Bearing grudges about it doesn't do anybody any good. It struck me that what was remarkable about that experience was not the feebleness of the human beings involved but the magnificent strength that in spite of bullets and shrapnel and things like that, human beings can endure and do endure.

No matter what people go into war thinking they're fighting for, ultimately when you get into combat you fight for completely different reasons. You fight in order to protect your buddies. That's why you form

5 **misanthropic:** having hatred or contempt for mankind

intense relationships in an atmosphere of death and self-preservation. When you're eighteen, nineteen, twenty years old, you've really emotionally separated yourself from your parents. You haven't yet acquired adult friends, an adult job, an adult milieu in which you move. You are betwixt and between. And so the friendships that you form, especially in combat, in the army, are very, very intense. That was the toughest thing I had to deal with after the war. These men, I really loved them, and they all got killed. Time heals. But I still remember them. I still go back to the Wall[6] and I say a prayer for them every once in a while. I still mourn them.

We all found it very hard to accept the pain and suffering that we went through when we ended up losing the war. What, then, in God's name, was the point of what we'd been doing in that landing zone? What in God's name was the point of the suffering that we went through? It was for nothing. If we didn't win the war, and if maybe we shouldn't have been there, then how do you justify the suffering, the loss of friends? You can't and that's what makes it tough for Vietnam veterans. ∾

---

6 **the Wall:** a reference to the Vietnam War Veterans Memorial in Washington, D.C.

BELLAMY 9   1988 Glenn Priestley

On the Rainy River

Tim O'Brien

This is one story I've never told before. Not to anyone. Not to my parents, not to my brother or sister, not even to my wife. To go into it, I've always thought, would only cause embarrassment for all of us, a sudden need to be elsewhere, which is the natural response to a confession. Even now, I'll admit, the story makes me squirm. For more than twenty years I've had to live with it, feeling the shame, trying to push it away, and so by this act of remembrance, by putting the facts down on paper, I'm hoping to relieve at least some of the pressure on my dreams. Still, it's a hard story to tell. All of us, I suppose, like to believe that in a moral emergency we will behave like the heroes of our youth, bravely and forthrightly, without thought of personal loss or discredit. Certainly that way my conviction back in the summer of 1968. Tim O'Brien: a secret hero. The Lone Ranger. If the stakes ever became high enough—if the evil were evil enough, if the good were good enough—I would simply tap a secret reservoir of courage that had been accumulating inside of me over the years. Courage, I seemed to think, comes to us in finite quantities, like an inheritance, and by being frugal and stashing it away and letting it earn interest, we steadily increase our moral capital in preparation for that day when the account must be drawn down. It was a comforting theory. It dispensed with all those bothersome little acts of daily courage; it offered hope and grace to the repetitive coward; it justified the past while amortizing the future.

In June of 1968, a month after graduating from Macalester College, I was drafted to fight a war I hated. I was twenty-one years old. Young, yes, and politically naive, but even so the American war in Vietnam seemed to me wrong. Certain blood was being shed for uncertain reasons. I saw no unity of purpose, no consensus on matters of philosophy or history or law. The very facts were shrouded in uncertainty: Was it a civil war? A war of national liberation or simple aggression? Who started it, and when, and why? What really happened to the USS *Maddox* on that dark night in the Gulf of Tonkin?[1] Was Ho Chi Minh a Communist stooge, or a nationalist savior, or both, or neither? What about the Geneva Accords? What about SEATO[2] and the Cold War? What about dominoes?[3] America was divided on these and a thousand other issues, and the debate had spilled out across the floor of the United States Senate and into the streets, and smart men in pinstripes could not agree on even the most fundamental matters of public policy. The only certainty that summer was moral confusion. It was my view then, and still is, that you don't make war without knowing why. Knowledge, of course, is always imperfect, but it seemed to me that when a nation goes to war it must have reasonable confidence in the justice and imperative of its cause. You can't fix your mistakes. Once people are dead, you can't make them undead.

In any case those were my convictions, and back in college I had taken a modest stand against the war. Nothing radical, no hothead stuff, just ringing a few doorbells for Gene McCarthy, composing a few tedious, uninspired editorials for the campus newspaper. Oddly, though, it was almost entirely an intellectual activity. I brought some energy to it, of course, but it was the energy that accompanies almost any abstract endeavor; I felt no personal danger; I felt no sense of an impending crisis in my life. Stupidly, with a kind of smug removal that I can't begin to fathom, I assumed that the problems of killing and dying did not fall within my special province.

The draft notice arrived on June 17, 1968. It was a humid afternoon, I remember, cloudy and very quiet, and I'd just come in from a round of golf. My mother and father were having lunch out in the kitchen. I remember opening up the letter, scanning the first few lines, feeling the

1 **USS Maddox . . . Gulf of Tonkin:** the alleged attack on the Maddox in the Gulf of Tonkin off the coast of Vietnam in 1964 gave President Johnson an excuse to expand U.S. involvement in the war

2 **SEATO:** Southeast Asia Treaty Organization; an alliance created in 1954 by the US and other Western and Southeast Asian countries to promote the region's defenses after the withdrawal of the French from Indochina

3 **dominoes:** a reference to the domino theory, which states that if one country falls to Communism, its neighbors would fall as well, like a row of dominoes

blood go thick behind my eyes. I remember a sound in my head. It wasn't thinking, it was just a silent howl. A million things all at once—I was too *good* for this war. Too smart, too compassionate, too everything. It couldn't happen. I was above it. A mistake, maybe—a foul-up in the paperwork. I was no soldier. I hated Boy Scouts. I hated camping out. I hated dirt and tents and mosquitoes. The sight of blood made me queasy, and I couldn't tolerate authority, and I didn't know a rifle from a slingshot. I was a *liberal*: If they needed fresh bodies, why not draft some back-to-the-stone-age hawk? Or some dumb jingo in his hard hat and Bomb Hanoi button. Or one of LBJ's pretty daughters? Or Westmoreland's whole family—nephews and nieces and baby grandson? There should be a law, I thought. If you support a war, if you think it's worth the price, that's fine, but you have to put your own life on the line. You have to head for the front and hook up with an infantry unit and help spill the blood. And you have to bring along your wife, your kids, or your lover. A *law*, I thought.

I remember the rage in my stomach. Later it burned down to a smoldering self-pity, then to numbness. At dinner that night my father asked what my plans were.

"Nothing," I said. "Wait."

▲　▲　▲

In the evenings I'd sometimes borrow my father's car and drive aimlessly around town, feeling sorry for myself, thinking about the war and the pig factory and how my life seemed to be collapsing toward slaughter. I felt paralyzed. All around me the options seemed to be narrowing, as if I were hurtling down a huge black funnel, the whole world squeezing in tight. There was no happy way out. The government had ended most graduate school deferments; the waiting lists for the National Guard and Reserves were impossibly long; my health was solid; I didn't qualify for CO[4] status—no religious grounds, no history as a pacifist. Moreover, I could not claim to be opposed to war as a matter of general principle. There were occasions, I believed, when a nation was justified in using military force to achieve its ends, to stop a Hitler or some comparable evil, and I told myself that in such circumstances I would've willingly marched off to the battle. The problem, though, was that a draft board did not let you choose your war.

4 **CO:** conscientious objector; someone exempted from military duty because his or her religious belief forbids participation in warfare

Beyond all this, or at the very center, was the raw fact of terror. I did not want to die. Not ever. But certainly not then, not there, not in the wrong war. Driving up Main Street, past the courthouse and the Ben Franklin store, I sometimes felt the fear spreading inside me like weeds. I imagined myself dead. I imagined myself doing things I could not do— charging an enemy position, taking aim at another human being.

At some point in mid-July I began thinking seriously about Canada. The border lay a few hundred miles north, an eight-hour drive. Both my conscience and my instincts were telling me to make a break for it, just take off and run like hell and never stop. In the beginning the idea seemed purely abstract, the word *Canada* printing itself out in my head; but after a time I could see particular shapes and images, the sorry details about my own future—a hotel room in Winnipeg, a battered old suitcase, my father's eyes as I tried to explain myself over the telephone. I could almost hear his voice, and my mother's. Run, I'd think. Then I'd think, Impossible. Then a second later I'd think, *Run*.

It was a kind of schizophrenia. A moral split. I couldn't make up my mind. I feared the war, yes, but I also feared exile. I was afraid of walking away from my own life, my friends and my family, my whole history, everything that mattered to me. I feared losing the respect of my parents. I feared the law. I feared ridicule and censure. My hometown was a conservative little spot on the prairie, a place where tradition counted, and it was easy to imagine people sitting around a table down at the old Gobbler Café on Main Street, coffee cups poised, the conversation slowly zeroing in on the young O'Brien kid, how the damned sissy had taken off for Canada. At night, when I couldn't sleep, I'd sometimes carry on fierce arguments with those people. I'd be screaming at them, telling them how much I detested their blind, thoughtless, automatic acquiescence to it all, their simple-minded patriotism, their prideful ignorance, their love-it-or-leave-it platitudes, how they were sending me off to fight a war they didn't understand. I held them responsible. By God, yes, I *did*. All of them—I held them personally and individually responsible—the polyestered Kiwanis boys, the merchants and farmers, the pious churchgoers, the chatty housewives, the PTA and the Lions club and the Veterans of Foreign Wars and the fine upstanding gentry out at the country club. They didn't know Bao Dai from the man in the moon. They didn't know history. They didn't know the first thing about Diem's tyranny, or the nature of Vietnamese nationalism, or the long colonialism of the French—this was all too complicated, it required some reading—but no matter, it was a war to stop the Communists, plain and simple, which was how they liked things, and you were treasonous if you had second thoughts about killing or dying for plain and simple reasons.

I was bitter, sure. But it was much more than that. The emotions went from outrage to terror to bewilderment to guilt to sorrow and then back again to outrage. I felt a sickness inside me. Real disease.

Most of this I've told before, or at least hinted at, but what I have never told before is the full truth. How I cracked. How at work one morning, standing on the pig line, I felt something break open in my chest. I don't know what it was. I'll never know. But it was real, I know that much, it was a physical rupture—a cracking-leaking-popping feeling. I remember dropping my water gun. Quickly, almost without thought, I took off my apron and walked out of the plant and drove home. It was midmorning, I remember, and the house was empty. Down in my chest there was still that leaking sensation, something very warm and precious spilling out, and I was covered with blood and hog-stink, and for a long while I just concentrated on holding myself together. I remember taking a hot shower. I remember packing a suitcase and carrying it out to the kitchen, standing very still for a few minutes, looking carefully at the familiar objects all around me. The old chrome toaster, the telephone, the pink and white Formica on the kitchen counters. The room was full of bright sunshine. Everything sparkled. My house, I thought. My life. I'm not sure how long I stood there, but later I scribbled out a short note to my parents.

What it said, exactly, I don't recall now. Something vague. Taking off, will call, love Tim.

▲ ▲ ▲

I drove north.

It's a blur now, as it was then, and all I remember is a sense of high velocity and the feel of the steering wheel in my hands. I was riding on adrenaline. A giddy feeling, in a way, except there was the dreamy edge of impossibility to it—like running a dead-end maze—no way out—it couldn't come to a happy conclusion and yet I was doing it anyway because it was all I could think of to do. It was pure flight, fast and mindless. I had no plan. Just hit the border at high speed and crash through and keep on running. Near dusk I passed through Bemidji, then turned northeast toward International Falls. I spent the night in the car behind a closed-down gas station a half mile from the border. In the morning, after gassing up, I headed straight west along the Rainy River, which separates Minnesota from Canada, and which for me separated one life from another. The land was mostly wilderness. Here and there I passed a motel or bait shop, but otherwise the country unfolded in great sweeps of pine and birch and sumac. Though it was still August, the air already had the smell of October, football season, piles of yellow-red leaves, everything crisp and clean. I remember a huge blue sky. Off to my right was the Rainy River, wide as a lake in places, and beyond the Rainy River was Canada.

For a while I just drove, not aiming at anything, then in the late morning I began looking for a place to lie low for a day or two. I was exhausted, and scared sick, and around noon I pulled into a old fishing resort called the Tip Top Lodge. Actually it was not a lodge at all, just eight or nine tiny yellow cabins clustered on a peninsula that jutted northward into the Rainy River. The place was in sorry shape. There was a dangerous wooden dock, an old minnow tank, a flimsy tar paper boathouse along the shore. The main building, which stood in a cluster of pines on high ground, seemed to lean heavily to one side, like a cripple, the roof sagging toward Canada. Briefly, I thought about turning around, just giving up, but then I got out of the car and walked up to the front porch.

The man who opened the door that day is the hero of my life. How do I say this without sounding sappy? Blurt it out—the man saved me. He offered exactly what I needed, without questions, without any words at all. He took me in. He was there at a critical time—a silent, watchful presence. Six days later, when it ended, I was unable to find a proper way to thank him, and I never have, and so, if nothing else, this story represents a small gesture of gratitude twenty years overdue.

Even after two decades I can close my eyes and return to that porch at the Tip Top Lodge. I can see the old guy staring at me. Elroy Berdahl: eighty-one years old, skinny and shrunken and mostly bald. He wore a flannel shirt and brown work pants. In one hand, I remember, he carried a green apple, a small paring knife in the other. His eyes had the bluish gray color of a razor blade, the same polished shine, and as he peered up at me I felt a strange sharpness, almost painful, a cutting sensation, as if his gaze were somehow slicing me open. In part, no doubt, it was my own sense of guilt, but even so I'm absolutely certain that the old man took one look and went right to the heart of things—a kid in trouble. When I asked for a room, Elroy made a little clicking sound with his tongue. He nodded, led me out to one of the cabins, and dropped a key in my hand. I remember smiling at him. I also

EMERSON   1986   Douglas Brega

remember wishing I hadn't. The old man shook his head as if to tell me
it wasn't worth the bother.

"Dinner at five-thirty," he said. "You eat fish?"

"Anything," I said.

Elroy grunted and said, "I'll bet."

▲ ▲ ▲

We spent six days together at the Tip Top Lodge. Just the two of us.
Tourist season was over, and there were no boats on the river, and the
wilderness seemed to withdraw into a great permanent stillness. Over
those six days, Elroy Berdahl and I took most of our meals together. In

the mornings we sometimes went out on long hikes into the woods, and at night we played Scrabble or listened to records or sat reading in front of his big stone fireplace. At times I felt the awkwardness of an intruder, but Elroy accepted me into his quiet routine without fuss or ceremony. He took my presence for granted, the same way he might've sheltered a stray cat—no wasted sighs or pity—and there was never any talk about it. Just the opposite. What I remember more than anything is the man's willful, almost ferocious silence. In all that time together, all those hours, he never asked the obvious questions: Why was I there? Why alone? Why so preoccupied? If Elroy was curious about any of this, he was careful never to put it into words.

My hunch, though, is that he already knew. At least the basics. After all, it was 1968, and guys were burning draft cards, and Canada was just a boat ride away. Elroy Berdahl was no hick. His bedroom, I remember, was cluttered with books and newspapers. He killed me at the Scrabble board, barely concentrating, and on those occasions when speech was necessary he had a way of compressing large thoughts into small, cryptic packets of language. One evening, just at sunset, he pointed up at an owl circling over the violet-lighted forest to the west.

"Hey, O'Brien," he said. "There's Jesus."

The man was sharp—he didn't miss much. Those razor eyes. Now and then he'd catch me staring out at the river, at the far shore, and I could almost hear the tumblers clicking in his head. Maybe I'm wrong, but I doubt it.

One thing for certain, he knew I was in desperate trouble. And he knew I couldn't talk about it. The wrong word—or even the right word—and I would've disappeared. I was wired and jittery. My skin felt too tight. After supper one evening I vomited and went back to my cabin and lay down for a few moments and then vomited again; another time, in the middle of the afternoon, I began sweating and couldn't shut it off. I went through whole days feeling dizzy with sorrow. I couldn't sleep; I couldn't lie still. At night I'd toss around in bed, half awake, half dreaming, imagining how I'd sneak down to the beach and quietly push one of the old man's boats out into the river and start paddling my way toward Canada. There were times when I'd thought I'd gone off the psychic edge. I couldn't tell up from down, I was just falling, and late in the night I'd lie there watching weird pictures spin though my head. Getting chased by the Border Patrol—helicopters and searchlights and barking dogs— I'd be crashing through the woods, I'd be down on my hands and knees—people shouting out my name—the law closing in on all sides—my hometown draft board and the FBI and the Royal Canadian Mounted Police. It all seemed crazy and impossible. Twenty-one years old, an ordinary kid with all the ordinary dreams and ambitions, and all I wanted was to live the life I was born to—a mainstream life—I loved baseball and hamburgers and cherry Cokes—and now I was off on the margins of exile, leaving my country forever, and it seemed so impossible and terrible and sad.

I'm not sure how I made it though those six days. Most of it I can't remember. On two or three afternoons, to pass some time, I helped Elroy get the place ready for winter, sweeping down the cabins and hauling in the boats, little chores that kept my body moving. The days were cool and bright. The nights were very dark. One morning the old man showed me how to split and stack firewood, and for several hours we just worked in silence out behind his house. At one point, I remember, Elroy put down his maul and looked at me for a long time, his lips drawn as if framing a difficult question, but then he shook his head and went back to work. The man's self-control was amazing. He never pried. He never put me in a position that required lies or denials. To an extent, I suppose, his reticence was typical of that part of Minnesota, where privacy still held value, and even if I'd been walking around with some horrible deformity—four arms and three heads—I'm sure the old man would've talked about everything except those extra arms and heads. Simple politeness was part of it. But even more than that, I think, the man understood that words were insufficient. The problem had gone beyond discussion. During that long summer I'd been over and over the various arguments, all the pros and cons, and it was no longer a question that could be decided by an act of pure reason. Intellect had come up against emotion. My conscience told me to run, but some irrational and powerful force was resisting, like a weight pushing me toward the war. What it came down to, stupidly, was a sense of shame. Hot, stupid shame. I did not want people to think badly of me. Not my parents, not to my brother and sister, not even the folks down at the Gobbler Café. I was ashamed to be there at the Tip Top Lodge. I was ashamed of my conscience, ashamed to be doing the right thing.

Some of this Elroy must've understood. Not the details, of course, but the plain fact of crisis.

Although the old man never confronted me about it, there was one occasion when he came close to forcing the whole thing out in the open.

It was early evening, and we'd just finished supper, and over coffee and dessert I asked him about my bill, how much I owed so far. For a long while the old man squinted down at the tablecloth.

"Well, the basic rate," he said, "is fifty bucks a night. Not counting meals. This makes four nights, right?"

I nodded. I had three hundred and twelve dollars in my wallet.

Elroy kept his eyes on the tablecloth. "Now that's an on-season price. To be fair, I suppose we should knock it down a peg or two." He leaned back in his chair. "What's a reasonable number, you figure?"

"I don't know," I said. "Forty?"

"Forty's good. Forty a night. Then we tack on food—say another hundred? Two hundred and sixty total?"

"I guess."

He raised his eyebrows. "Too much?"

"No, that's fair. It's fair. Tomorrow, though . . . I think I'd better take off tomorrow."

Elroy shrugged and began clearing the table. For a time he fussed with the dishes, whistling to himself as if the subject had been settled. After a second he slapped his hands together.

"You know what we forgot?" he said. "We forgot wages. Those odd jobs you've done. What we have to do, we have to figure out what your time's worth. Your last job—how much did you pull in an hour?"

"Not enough," I said.

"A bad one?"

"Yes. Pretty bad."

Slowly then, without intending any long sermon, I told him about my days at the pig plant. It began as a straight recitation of the facts, but before I could stop myself I was talking about the blood clots and the water gun and how the smell had soaked into my skin and how I couldn't wash it away. I went on for a long time. I told him about wild hogs squealing in my dreams, the sounds of butchery, slaughterhouse sounds, and how I'd sometimes wake up with that greasy pig-stink in my throat.

When I was finished, Elroy nodded at me.

"Well, to be honest," he said, "when you first showed up here, I wondered about all that. The aroma, I mean. Smelled like you was awful fond of pork chops." The old man almost smiled. He made a snuffling sound, then sat down with a pencil and a piece of paper. "So what'd this crud job pay? Ten bucks an hour? Fifteen?"

"Less."

Elroy shook his head. "Let's make it fifteen. You put in twenty-five hours here, easy. That's three hundred seventy-five bucks total wages. We subtract two hundred sixty for food and lodging, I still owe you hundred and fifteen."

He took four fifties out of his shirt pocket and laid them on the table.

"Call it even."

"No."

"Pick it up. Get yourself a haircut."

The money lay on the table for the rest of the evening. It was still there when I went back to my cabin. In the morning, though, I found an envelope tacked to my door. Inside were the four fifties and a two-word note that said EMERGENCY FUND.

The man knew.

▲ ▲ ▲

Looking back after twenty years, I sometimes wonder if the events of that summer didn't happen in some other dimension, a place where your life exists before you've lived it, and where it goes afterward. None of it ever seemed real. During my time at the Tip Top Lodge I had the feeling that I'd slipped out of my own skin, hovering a few feet away while some poor yo-yo with my name and face tried to make his way toward a future he didn't understand and didn't want. Even now I can see myself as I was then. It's like watching an old home movie: I'm young and tan and fit. I've got hair—lots of it. I don't smoke or drink. I'm wearing faded blue jeans and a white polo shirt. I can see myself sitting on Elroy Berdahl's dock near dusk one evening, the sky a bright shimmering pink, and I'm finishing up a letter to my parents that tells them what I'm about to do and why I'm doing it and how sorry I am that I'd never found the courage to talk to them about it. I ask them not to be angry. I try to explain some of my feelings, but there aren't enough words, and so I just say that it's a thing that has to be done. At the end of the letter I talk about the vacations we used to take up in this north county, at a place called Whitefish Lake, and how the scenery here reminds me of those good times. I tell them I'm fine. I tell them I'll write again from Winnipeg or Montreal or wherever I end up.

▲ ▲ ▲

On my last full day, the sixth day, the old man took me out fishing on the Rainy River. The afternoon was sunny and cold. A still breeze came in from the north, and I remember how the little fourteen-foot boat made sharp rocking motions as we pushed off from the dock. The current was fast. All around us, I remember, there was a vastness to the world, an unpeopled rawness, just the trees and the sky and the water reaching out toward nowhere. The air had the brittle scent of October.

For ten or fifteen minutes Elroy held a course upstream, the river choppy and silver-gray, then he turned straight north and put the engine on full throttle. I felt the bow lift beneath me. I remember the wind in my ears, the sound of the old outboard Evinrude. For a time I didn't pay attention to anything, just feeling the cold spray against my face, but then it occurred to me that at some point we must've passed into Canadian waters, across that dotted line between two different worlds, and I remember a sudden tightness in my chest as I looked up and watched the far shore come at me. This wasn't a daydream. It was tangible and real. As we came in toward land, Elroy cut the engine, letting the boat fishtail lightly about twenty yards off shore. The old man didn't look at me or speak. Bending down, he opened up his tackle box and busied himself with a bobber and a piece of wire leader, humming to himself, his eyes down.

It struck me that he must've planned it. I'll never be certain, of course, but I think he meant to bring me up against the realities, to guide me across the river and to take me the to the edge and to stand a kind of vigil as I chose a life for myself.

I remember staring at the old man, then at my hands, then at Canada. The shoreline was dense with brush and timber. I could see tiny red berries on the bushes. I could see a squirrel up in one of the birch trees, a big crow looking at me from a boulder along the river. That close—twenty yards—and I could see the delicate latticework of the leaves, the texture of the soil, the browned needles beneath the pines, the configurations of geology and human history. Twenty yards. I could've done it. I could've jumped and started swimming for my life. Inside me, in my chest, I felt a terrible squeezing pressure. Even now, as I write this, I can still feel that tightness. And I want you to feel it—the wind coming off the river, the waves, the silence, the wooded frontier. You're at the bow of a boat on the Rainy River. You're twenty-one years old, you're scared, and there's a hard squeezing pressure in your chest.

What would you do?

Would you jump? Would you feel pity for yourself? Would you think about your family and your childhood and your dreams and all you're leaving behind? Would it hurt? Would it feel like dying? Would you cry, as I did?

I tried to swallow it back. I tried to smile, except I was crying.

Now, perhaps, you can understand why I've never told this story before. It's not just the embarrassment of tears. That's part of it, no doubt, but what embarrasses me much more, and always will, is the paralysis that took my heart. A moral freeze: I couldn't decide, I couldn't act, I couldn't comport myself with even a pretense of modest human dignity.

All I could do was cry. Quietly, not bawling, just the chest-chokes.

At the rear of the boat Elroy Berdahl pretended not to notice. He held a fishing rod in his hands, his head bowed to hide his eyes. He kept humming a soft, monotonous little tune. Everywhere, it seemed, in the trees and water and sky, a great worldwide sadness came pressing down on me, a crushing sorrow, sorrow like I had never known it before. And what was so sad, I realized, was that Canada had become a pitiful fantasy. Silly and hopeless. It was no longer a possibility. Right then, with the shore so close, I understood that I would not do what I should do. I would not swim away from my hometown and my country and my life. I would not be brave. That old image of myself as a hero, as a man of conscience and courage, all that was just a threadbare pipe dream. Bobbing there on the Rainy River, looking back at the Minnesota shore, I felt a sudden swell of helplessness come over me, a drowning sensation, as if I had toppled overboard and was being swept away by the silver waves. Chunks of my own history flashed by. I saw a seven-year-old boy in a white cowboy hat and a Lone Ranger mask and a pair of holstered six-shooters; I saw a twelve-year-old Little League shortstop pivoting to turn a double play; I saw a sixteen-year-old kid decked out for his first prom, looking spiffy in a white tux and a black bow tie, his hair cut short and flat, his shoes freshly polished. My whole life seemed to spill out into the river, swirling away from me, everything I had ever been or ever wanted to be. I couldn't get my breathe; I couldn't stay afloat; I couldn't tell which way to swim. A hallucination, I suppose, but it was as real as anything I would ever feel. I saw my parents calling to me from the far shoreline. I saw my brother and sister, all the townsfolk, the mayor and the entire Chamber of Commerce and all my old teachers and girlfriends and high school buddies. Like some weird sporting event: everybody screaming from the sidelines, rooting me on—a loud stadium roar. Hotdogs and popcorn— stadium smells, stadium heat. A squad of cheerleaders did cartwheels along the banks of the Rainy River; they had megaphones and pompoms and smooth brown thighs. The crowd swayed right and left. A marching band played fight songs. All my aunts and uncles were there, and Abraham Lincoln, and Saint George, and a nine-year-old girl named Linda who had died of brain tumor back in fifth grade, and several members of the United States Senate, and a blind poet scribbling notes, and LBJ, and Huck Finn, and Abbie Hoffman, and all the dead soldiers back from the grave, and the many thousands who were later to die—villagers with terrible burns, little kids without arms or legs—yes, and the Joint Chiefs of Staff were there, and a couple of popes, and a first lieutenant named Jimmy Cross, and the last surviving veteran of the American Civil War, and Jane Fonda dressed up as Barbarella, and an old man sprawled beside a pigpen, and my grandfather, and Gary Cooper, and a kind-faced woman carrying an umbrella and a copy of Plato's *Republic*, and a million ferocious citizens waving flags of all shapes and colors—people in hard hats, people in headbands—they were all whooping and chanting and urging me toward one shore or the other. I saw faces from my distant past and distant future. My wife was there. My unborn daughter waved at me, and my two sons hopped up and down, and a drill sergeant named Blyton sneered and shot up a finger and shook his head. There was a choir in bright purple robes. There was a cabbie from the Bronx. There was a slim young man I would one day kill with a hand grenade along a red clay trail outside the village of My Khe.

The little aluminum boat rocked softly beneath me. There was the wind and the sky.

I tried to will myself overboard.

I gripped the edge of the boat and leaned forward and thought, *Now*.

I did try. It just wasn't possible.

All those eyes on me—the town, the whole universe—and I couldn't risk the embarrassment. It was as if there were an audience to my life, that swirl of faces along the river, and in my head I could hear people screaming at me. Traitor! they yelled. Turncoat! I felt myself blush. I couldn't tolerate it. I couldn't endure the mockery, or the disgrace, or the patriotic ridicule. Even in my imagination, the shore just twenty yards away, I couldn't make myself be brave. it had nothing to do with morality. Embarrassment, that's all it was.

And right then I submitted.

I would go to the war—I would kill and maybe die—because I was embarrassed not to.

That was the sad thing. And so I sat in the bow of the boat and cried. It was loud now. Loud, hard crying.

Elroy Berdahl remained quiet. He kept fishing. He worked his line with the tips of his fingers, patiently, squinting out at his red and white bobber on the Rainy River. His eyes were flat and impassive. He didn't speak. He was simply there, like the river and the late-summer sun. And yet by his presence, his mute watchfulness, he made it real. He was the true audience. He was a witness, like God, or like the gods, who look on in absolute silence as we live our lives, as we make our choices or fail to make them.

"Ain't biting," he said.

Then after a time the old man pulled in his line and turned the boat back toward Minnesota. ⌒

BOUNDARY LAKE 1995 Ken Moylan

Responding to Cluster One

What Were the Roots of the Conflict?

Thinking Skill SUMMARIZING

1. What does the poem "History" tell you about Vietnam's past?

2. The main characters (or speakers) in this cluster express definite opinions about the conflict in Vietnam. Using a chart such as the one below, **summarize** these opinions.

Individual	Summary Sentence
Speaker of "Ballad of the Green Berets"	
Speaker of "History"	
Author of "Gulf of Tonkin Resolution May Have Been the Gulf Between Truth and Fiction"	
Jack Smith	
Narrator of "On the Rainy River"	

3. Compare Jack Smith's attitude toward the war at the beginning with his attitude at the conclusion of his story.

4. Near the end of the short story "On the Rainy River," Tim O'Brien calls himself a coward. Do you agree with his assessment? Why or why not?

5. How did the United States government justify its military involvement in Vietnam?

Writing Activity: A Poetic Summary

The poem "History" summarizes centuries of conflict in thirty-one lines. Using the information in this cluster and what you already know, write a poem that summarizes some aspect of the war in Vietnam.

A poem

• places emphasis on language as well as the topic.

• may employ rhythm and/or rhyme.

• may use figurative language (similes, metaphors, and personification).

• chooses words carefully in order to convey meanings and feelings

CLUSTER TWO

What Was the War Experience?
Thinking Skill ANALYZING

I-Feel-Like-I'm-Fixin'-To-Die Rag

JOE MCDONALD

Yeah, come on all of you big strong men,
Uncle Sam needs your help again.
He's got himself in a terrible jam
Way down yonder in Vietnam
So put down your books and pick up a gun,
We're gonna have a whole lotta fun.

And it's one, two, three,
What are we fighing for?
Don't ask me, I don't give a damn,
Next stop is Vietnam:
And it's five, six, seven,
Open up the pearly gates,
Well there ain't no time to wonder why,
Whoopee! we're all gonna die.

Well, come on generals, let's move fast;
Your big chance has come at last.
Gotta go out and get those reds—
The only good commie is the one who's dead
And you know that peace can only be won
When we've blown 'em all to kingdom come.

And it's one, two, three,
What are we fighting for?
Don't ask me, I don't give a damn,
Next stop is Vietnam;
And it's five, six, seven,
Open up the pearly gates,
Well there ain't no time to wonder why
Whoopee! we're all gonna die.

Huh!

Well, come on Wall Street, don't move slow,
Why man, this is war au-go-go.
There's plenty good money to be made
By supplying the Army with the tools of the trade,
Just hope and pray that if they drop the bomb,
They drop it on the Viet Cong.

And it's one, two, three,
What are we fighting for?
Don't ask me, I don't give a damn,
Next stop is Vietnam.
And it's five, six, seven,
Open up the pearly gates,
Well there ain't no time to wonder why
Whoopee! we're all gonna die.

Well, come on mothers throughout the land,
Pack your boys off to Vietnam
Come on fathers, don't hesitate
Send 'em off before it's too late.
Be the first one on your block
To have your boy come home in a box.

And it's one, two, three,
What are we fighting for?
Don't ask me, I don't give a damn,
Next stop is Vietnam.
And it's five, six, seven,
Open up the pearly gates,
Well there ain't no time to wonder why,
Whoopee! we're all gonna die.

The Grateful Dead

Hippies
1967, San Francisco

ALEX FORMAN

When I came to San Francisco, the city was just exploding with this counterculture movement. I thought, "This is it!" It was like paradise there. Everybody was in love with life and in love with their fellow human beings to the point where they were just sharing in incredible ways with everybody. Taking people in off the street and letting them stay in their homes, breaking free of conventional morality. You could walk down almost any street in Haight-Ashbury where I was living, and someone would smile at you and just go, "Hey, it's beautiful, isn't it?" It was like people were high on the street and willing to share that energy. It was a very special time.

It was a whole other vision of what was possible. Rents were cheap and people were living in big communal groups, and we didn't have to work very hard. There was a sense that you didn't need very much, and that people who worked hard were just trapped into trying to acquire more and more possessions. People should just begin more to enjoy life, play music, dance, experience nature. We were going to raise our kids communally and all that stuff, and such attitudes would flourish even more. I thought this was the new world beginning right here—an alternative society—and this was where I wanted to be. So I stayed.

The first human Be-In was in January of '67 in Golden Gate Park. That was a very high moment. People went and just kind of experienced. A lot of people were on LSD or peyote or marijuana. They played music, shared food, played drums, did American Indian chanting. You know, tie-dyed clothes, the whole thing. It all seems very trite now, but at the time it was all new. People were coming from all over the world to

(FX 2) SAN FRANCISCO,OCT.6-(AP)-A large group of hippies greet the sunrise from a San Francisco hilltop on Friday beginning a three-day wake for the death of the hippie movement in the Haight-Ashbury district. Summer hippies have been pouring out of town. More are expected go as San Francisco's chilly fall sets in. It is not the climate for bare feet and sleeping in the park, a policeman said, and we could use some bad weather to speed them on their way. (AP Wirephoto)1967

research it, to experience it. People from Czechoslovakia, Australia, Finland. It was a real phenomenon.

For a while I worked with a group in the Haight called the Diggers, who had a kind of a primitive communism view that was just "share all the wealth." The Diggers set up a free store, and people could just come in and take whatever they needed, and we fed people for free in the park. At one point I realized the absurdity of that when these people from the neighborhood, these older black women, came into the free store and said, "How much do these clothes cost in here?"

We said, "Oh, it's all free. You just take what you need, and then if you have extra, you give."

They said, "What do you mean, you just take what you need?"

"Well, you just take what you need, that's all."

They said, "Really?"

So they came back with these big boxes and they started just taking tons of stuff off the racks.

We said, "What are you doing?"

They said, "Well, you said take what you need."

We said, "Yeah, well, you don't need all those clothes for yourself."

They said, "No, but we need the money, so we're going to take the clothes and sell them."

They were in real scarcity, you know, they needed money, and here we were saying just take what you need for your own personal, immediate needs. But for them, that wasn't reality. Their reality was, "How are we going to get some money, and here's these foolish white people just letting us take whatever we need. Well, we need it all. We don't have anything."

That was the illusion of the whole hippie ethos, that there was this abundance. I think the hippie movement started in California—and was most powerful here—because there is this illusion of abundance here. Fruits were falling from the trees, rent was cheap, there were places to stay, the weather was tolerable even in the winter, there was a community of people who were into sharing. But there wasn't an abundance. There was an abundance at a certain time for certain people.

In early 1967, people would just give things away. On every street corner, there would be somebody giving things away, free food, a free place to stay. Then in the summer of '67 was the Summer of Love. People started storming in by the thousands, and within three months there were people begging, "Do you have free food?" In other words, so many came that the surplus changed to scarcity. It got very ugly very fast. People got into really bad drugs like speed and heroin. There were ripoffs, violence, guns being drawn, people really malnourished, hepatitis, people living on the street with no place to stay.

I quickly saw then that the counterculture wasn't going to make it. It wasn't going to work. It was an illusion. And meanwhile the war was going on. It became more and more clear that you couldn't just set up little islands of peace and love in the middle of the Vietnam War. ∾

Village

ESTELA PORTILLO

Rico stood on top of a bluff overlooking Mai Cao. The whole of the wide horizon was immersed in a rosy haze. His platoon was returning from an all-night patrol. They had scoured the area in a radius of thirty-two miles, following the length of the canal system along the delta, furtively on the lookout for an enemy attack. On their way back they had stopped to rest, smoke, drink warm beer after parking the carryalls along the edge of the climb leading to the top of the bluff. The hill was good cover, seemingly safe.

Harry was behind him on the rocky slope. Then, the sound of thunder overhead. It wasn't thunder, but a squadron of their own helicopters on the usual run. Rico and Harry sat down to watch the planes go by. After that, a stillness, a special kind of silence. Rico knew it well, the same kind of stillness that was a part of him back home, the kind of stillness that makes a man part of his world—river, clearing, sun, wind. The stillness of a village early in the morning—barrio stillness, the first stirrings of life that come with dawn. Harry was looking down at the village of Mai Cao.

"Makes me homesick . . ." Harry lighted a cigarette.

Rico was surprised. He thought Harry was a city dude. Chicago, no less. "I don't see no freeway or neon lights."

"I'm just sick of doing nothing in this damned war."

No action yet. But who wanted action? Rico had been transformed into a soldier, but he knew he was no soldier. He had been trained to kill the enemy in Vietnam. He watched the first curl of smoke coming out of one of the chimneys. They were the enemy down there. Rico didn't believe it. He would never believe it. Perhaps because there had been no confrontation with Viet Cong soldiers or village people. Harry flicked away his cigarette and started down the slope. He turned, waiting for Rico to follow him. "Coming?"

"I'll be down after a while."

"Suit yourself." Harry walked swiftly down the bluff, his feet carrying with them the dirt yieldings in a flurry of small pebbles and loose earth. Rico was relieved. He needed some time by himself, to think things out. But Harry was right. To come across an ocean just to do routine checks, to patrol ground where there was no real danger . . . it could get pretty bad. The enemy was hundreds of miles away.

The enemy! He remembered the combat bible—kill or be killed. Down a man—the lethal lick: a garrote strangling is neater and more quiet than the slitting of a throat; grind your heel against a face to mash the brains. Stomp the rib cage to carve the heart with bone splinters. Kill . . .

Hey, who was kidding who? They almost made him believe it back at boot camp in the States. In fact, only a short while ago, only that morning he had crouched down along the growth following a mangrove swamp, fearing an unseen enemy, ready to kill. Only that morning. But now, looking down at the peaceful village with its small rice field, its scattered huts, something had struck deep, something beyond the logic of war and enemy, something deep in his guts.

He had been cautioned. The rows of thatched huts were not really peoples' homes, but "hootches," makeshift temporary stays built by the makeshift enemy. But then they were the real enemies. There were too many dead Americans to prove it. The hootches didn't matter. The people didn't matter. These people knew how to pick up their sticks and go. Go where? Then how many of these villages had been bulldozed? Flattened by gunfire? Good pyre for napalm, these Vietnamese villages. A new kind of battleground.

Rico looked down and saw huts that were homes, clustered in an intimacy that he knew well. The village of Mai Cao was no different than Valverde, the barrio where he had grown up. A woman came out of a hut, walking straight and with a certain grace, a child on her shoulder. She was walking toward a stream east of the slope. She stopped along the path and looked up to say something to the child. It struck him again, the feeling—a bond—people all the same everywhere.

The same scent from the earth, the same warmth from the sun, a woman walking with a child—his mother, Trini. His little mother who had left Tarahumara County and crossed the Barranca del Cobre, taking with her seeds from the hills of Batophilas, withstanding suffering, danger—for what? A dream—a piece of ground in the land of plenty, the United States of America. She had waded across the Rio Grande from Juárez, Mexico, to El Paso, Texas, when she felt the birth pangs of his coming. He had been born a citizen because his mother had had a dream. She had made the dream come true—an acre of river land in Valverde, on the edge of the border. His mother, like the earth and sun, mattered. The woman with the child on her shoulder mattered. Every human life in the village mattered. He knew this not only with the mind but with the heart.

Rico remembered a warning from combat training, from the weary, wounded soldiers who had fought and killed and survived, soldiers sent to Saigon, waiting to go home. His company had been flown to Saigon before being sent to the front. And this was the front, villages like Mai Cao. He felt relieved knowing that the fighting was hundreds of miles away from the people in Mai Cao—but the warning was still there:

Watch out for pregnant women with machine guns. Toothless old women are experts with the knife between the shoulders. Begging children with hidden grenades, the unseen VC hiding it the hootches—village people were not people; they were the enemy. The woman who knew the child on her shoulder, who knew the path to her door, who knew the coming of the sun—she was the enemy.

It was a discord not to be believed by instinct or intuition. And Rico was an Indian, the son of a Tarahumara chieftain. Theirs was a world of instinct and intuitive decisions. Suddenly he heard the sounds of motors. He looked to the other side of the slope, down to the road where the carryalls had started queuing their way back to the post. Rico ran down the hill to join his company.

In his dream, Sergeant Keever was shouting, "Heller, heller . . ." Rico woke with a start. It wasn't a dream. The men around him were scrambling out of the pup tent. Outside, most of the men were lining up in uneven formation. Rico saw a communiqué in the sergeant's hand. Next to Keever was a lieutenant from communications headquarters. Keever was reading the communiqué.

"Special mission 72 . . . for Company C, platoon 2, assigned at 22 hours. Moving into the village of Mai Cao, field manual description—hill 72. Destroy the village."

No! It was crazy. Why? Just words on a piece of paper. Keever had to tell him why. There had to be a reason. Had the enemy come this far? It was impossible. Only that morning he had stood on the slope. He caught up with Keever, blurting it out. "Why? I mean—why must we destroy it?"

Sergeant Keever stopped in his tracks and turned steel blue eyes at Rico. "What you say?"

"Why?"

"You just follow orders, savvy?"

"Are the Viet Cong . . ."

"Did you hear me? You want trouble, Private?"

"There's people . . ."

"I don't believe you, soldier. But OK. Tell you as much as I know. We gotta erase the village in case the Viet Cong come this way. That way they won't use it as a stronghold. Now move . . ."

Keever walked away from him, his lips tight in some kind of disgust. Rico did not follow this time. He went to get his gear and join the men in one of the carryalls. Three carryalls for the assault—three carryalls moving up the same road. Rico felt the weight and hardness of his carbine. Now it had a strange, hideous meaning. The machine guns were some kind of nightmare. The mission was to kill and burn and erase all memories. Rico swallowed a guilt that rose from the marrow—with it, all kinds of fear. He had to do something, something to stop it, but he didn't know what. And with all these feelings, a certain reluctance to do anything but follow orders. In the darkness, his lips formed the words from the anthem, "My country, 'tis of thee . . ."

They came to the point where the tree lines straggled between two hills that rose darkly against the moon. Rico wondered if all the men were of one mind—one mind to kill . . . Was he a coward? No! It was not killing the enemy that his whole being was rejecting, but firing machine guns into a village of sleeping people . . . people. Rico remembered only the week before, returning from their usual patrol, the men from the company had stopped at the stream, mingling with the children, old men, and women of the village. There had been an innocence about the whole thing. His voice broke the silence in the carryall, a voice harsh and feverish, "We can get the people out of there. Help them evacuate . . ."

"Shut up," Harry's voice was tight, impatient.

The carryalls traveled through tall, undulant grass following the dirt road that led to the edge of the bluff. It was not all tall grass. Once in a while trees appeared again, clumped around scrub bushes. Ten miles out the carryalls stopped. It was still a mile's walk to the bluff in the darkness, but they had to avoid detection. Sergeant Keever was leading the party. Rico, almost at the rear, knew he had to catch up to him. He had to stop him. Harry was ahead of him, a silent black bundle walking stealthily though rutted ground to discharge his duty. For a second, Rico hesitated. That was the easy thing to do—to carry out his duty—to die a hero, to do his duty blindly and survive. Hell, why not? He knew what happened to men who backed down in battle. But he wasn't backing down. Hell, what else was it? How often had he heard it among the gringos in his company?

"You Mexican? Hey, you Mexicans are real fighters. I mean, everybody knows Mexicans have guts . . ."

A myth perhaps. But no. He thought of the old guys who had fought in World War II. Many of them were on welfare back in the barrio. But, man! Did they have medals! He had never seen so many purple hearts. He remembered old Toque, the wino, who had tried to pawn his medals to buy a bottle. No way, man. They weren't worth a nickel.

He quickly edged past Harry, pushing the man ahead of him to reach the sergeant. He was running, tall grass brushing his shoulder, tall grass that swayed peacefully like wheat. The figure of Sergeant Keever was in front of him now. There was a sudden impulse to reach out and hold him back. But the sergeant had stopped. Rico did not touch him but whispered hoarsely, desperately in the dark. "Let's get the people out—evacuate . . ."

"What the hell . . ." Keever's voice was ice. He recognized Rico and hissed, "Get back to your position, soldier, or I'll shoot you myself."

Rico did as he was told, almost unaware of the men around him. But at a distance he heard something splashing in the water of the canal, in his nostrils the smell of sweet burnt wood. He looked toward the clearing and saw the cluster of huts bathed in the moonlight. In the same moonlight, he saw Keever giving signals. In the gloom, he saw the figures of the men carrying machine guns. They looked like dancing grasshoppers as they ran ahead to position themselves on the bluff. He felt like yelling, "For Christ's sake! Where is the enemy?"

The taste of blood in his mouth—he suddenly realized he had bitten his quivering lower lip. As soon as Sergeant Keever gave the signal, all sixteen men would open fire on the huts—machine guns, carbines— everything would be erased. No more Mai Cao—the execution of duty without question, without alternative. They were positioned on the south slope, Sergeant Keever up ahead, squatting on his heels, looking at his watch. He raised himself, after a quick glance at the men. As Sergeant

Keever raised his hand to give the signal for attack, Rico felt the cold metallic deadness of his rifle. His hands began to tremble as his released the safety catch. Sergeant Keever was on the rise just above him. Rico stared at the sergeant's arm, raised, ready to fall—the signal to fire. The cross-fire was inside Rico, a heavy-dosed tumult—destroy the village, erase all memory. There was ash in his mouth. Once the arm came down, there was no turning back.

In a split second, Rico turned his rifle at a forty-degree angle and fired at the sergeant's arm. Keever half turned with the impact of the bullet, then fell to his knees. In a whooping whisper the old-time soldier blew out the words, "That . . . —get him." He got up and signaled the platoon back to the carryalls as two men grabbed Rico, one hitting him on the side of the head with the butt of his rifle. Rico felt the sting of the blow as they pinned his arm back and forced him to walk the path back to the carryall. He did not resist. There was a lump in his throat, tears of relief. The memory of the village would not be erased. Someone shouted in the dark, "They're on to us. There's an old man with a lantern and others coming out of the hootches . . ."

"People—just people . . ." Rico whispered, wanting to shout it, wanting to tell them that he had done the right thing. But the heaviness that filled his senses was the weight of the truth. He was a traitor—a maniac. He had shot his superior in a battle crisis. He was being carried almost bodily back to the truck. He glanced back at the thick brush along the road, thinking that somewhere beyond it was a rice field, and beyond that a mangrove swamp. There was a madman inside his soul that made him think of rice fields and mangrove swamps instead of what he had done. Not once did he look up. Everyone around him was strangely quiet and remote. Only the sound of trudging feet.

In the carryall, the faces of the men sitting around Rico were indiscernible in the dark, but he imagined their eyes, wide, confused, peering through the dark at him with a wakefulness that questioned what he had done. Did they know his reason? Did they care? The truck suddenly lurched. Deep in the gut, Rico felt a growing fear. He choked back a hysteria rising from the diaphragm. The incessant bumping of the carryalls as they moved unevenly on the dirt road accused him too. He looked up into a night sky and watched the moon eerily weave in and out of tree branches. The darkness was like his fear. It had no solutions.

Back on the post, Sergeant Keever and a medic passed by Rico, already handcuffed, without any sign of recognition. Sergeant Keever had already erased him from existence. The wheels of justice would take their course. Rico had been placed under arrest, temporarily shackled to a cot in one of the tents. Three days later he was moved to makeshift bamboo hut, with a guard in front of the hut at all times. His buddies brought in food like strangers, awkward in their silence, anxious to leave him alone. He felt like some kind of poisonous bug. Only Harry came by to see him after a week.

"You dumb jerk, were you on locoweed?" Harry asked in disgust.

"I didn't want people killed, that's all."

"Hell, that's no reason, those chinks aren't even—even . . ."

"Even what?" Rico demanded. He almost screamed it a second time. "Even what?"

"Take it easy, will you? You better go for a Section 8."[1] Harry was putting him aside like everyone else. "They're sending you back to the States next week. You'll have to face Keever sometime this afternoon. I thought I'd better let you know."

"Thanks." Rico knew the hopelessness of it all. There was still that nagging question he had to ask. "Listen, nobody tells me anything. Did you all go back to Mai Cao? I mean, is it still there?"

"Still there. Orders from headquarters to forget it. The enemy were spotted taking an opposite direction. But nobody's going to call you a hero, you understand? What you did was crud. You're no soldier. You'll never be a soldier."

Rico said nothing to defend himself. He began to scratch the area around the steel rings on his ankles. Harry was scowling at him. He said it again, almost shouting, "I said, you'll never be a soldier."

"So?" There was a soft disdain in Rico's voice.

"You blew it, man. You'll be locked up for a long, long time."

"Maybe . . ." Rico's voice was without concern.

"Don't you care?"

"I'm free inside, Harry." Rico laughed in relief. "Free . . ."

Harry shrugged, peering at Rico unbelievingly, then turned and walked out of the hut. ∾

---

1 **Section 8:** a discharge from the U.S. Army for military inaptitude or undesirable habits

Farmer Nguyen

W. D. Ehrhart

When we swept through farmer Nguyen's hamlet,
some people said that farmer Nguyen
had given rice to the Vietcong.

> You picked the wrong side, farmer Nguyen.
> We took you in, and beat you,
> and put you in a barbed wire cage.

When the Vietcong returned to farmer Nguyen's hamlet,
some people said that farmer Nguyen
had given information to the Round Eyes.

> Wrong again, farmer Nguyen.
> They took more rice, beat you,
> and made you carry supplies.

The Massacre at My Lai

HUGH THOMPSON

*My Lai was a wartime atrocity. The massacre of an estimated 347
unarmed Vietnamese villagers by American soldiers was covered up by
the military. One soldier felt the story should be told, and he wrote to
government officials until an investigation was opened. The slaughter
of the innocent helped turn the tide of public opinion against the
war in the United States.*

I arrived over My Lai, which was better known as Pinkville, at about
7:20 in the morning. I was flying a Scout helicopter and my job was to
draw out enemy fire. We had been briefed the night before that there had
been a large enemy buildup in the area. But so far, we only saw one draft-
age male running out of the village with a weapon. I told my door
gunner, Lawrence Colburn, to fire at him. He missed. That was the only
enemy person we saw all day.

We were flying back and forth for some time, not getting shot at,
when I left to refuel. When we got back on station there were bodies
everywhere. These were infants and toddlers, women and very old
men—but no young men. On one pass just outside the village, we saw a
teenage girl lying on her back in a rice field. She was flailing back and
forth, obviously wounded. I hovered over her, marked her with a smoke
flare and got on the radio to call for help. A captain approached. He
nudged her with his foot, then stood back, put his weapon on automatic,
and blew her away. We didn't know what to think of that.

My Lai villagers moments before being
fired on by U.S. troops.

We came across a ditch that had a large number of people in it who appeared to be injured. We noticed babies, women and children and old men. I put the helicopter down, then went over to ask a sergeant to help them out. He said the only way to do that was to put them out of their misery. I thought he was joking. We took off and heard shots right away. My crew chief, Glenn Andreotta, yelled, "My God, they are firing into the ditch." I swung the Scout around so all of us could see. They were standing around, just firing. We said, "My God, what is happening here?" We ran some scenarios through our minds, but we didn't want to condemn our own people. But it sunk into me that these people were marched into that ditch and murdered.

A few minutes later I saw some people huddled by a bunker. There was a woman, an old man and a couple of kids with her. We saw some advancing American forces coming at them, being led, I was told later, by William Calley (who was ultimately court-martialed). I said the Vietnamese have only about 15 seconds to live. I sat the chopper down between the civilians and the advancing Americans. I told Colburn to blow 'em away if they began to fire at the civilians. I thank God that they didn't. I went over to the officer in charge and said there are some civilians in here, can you get them out? He said a hand grenade would do the job. I said, "You see my guns? If you open up, they open up." I coaxed about 10 people out of the bunker, then called a friend flying a bigger chopper to take them away.

We made a final pass over the ditch. Glenn yelled that something was moving. I set the helicopter down and Glenn ran over to the ditch. Larry and I covered him with our weapons. He waded in among the dead and bloodied people, and pulled out a little boy, about the same age as my son, who was 4 at the time. The boy was covered in blood, but he didn't have a scratch on him. We got back in and laid the kid over our laps. As we flew to a nearby orphanage, tears were streaming down our cheeks. I flew back to base and confronted my superiors. It would take time, but the horrible killing at My Lai would become public. My Lai was no accident. It was pure, premeditated murder. ☙

A Nun in Ninh Hoa

JAN BERRY

It was quite a sight for a boy from Tennessee:
a Buddhist nun dressed in fire
sitting proudly amid a solemn, silent crowd,
flames and a smoke plume her terrible costume.

Riding shotgun on a fuel truck convoy,
"just along for the ride,"
Jimmy Sharpe saw a sight the morning
beyond any experience he can describe.

She sat smiling as though mocking the flames.
Her hands, held together in prayer,
slowly parted. Suddenly, she drooped,
sat up, then wilted in the fire.

Safe back at the base, Jimmy's chatter
circled the nightmare he could still taste.
He grinned   shivered—then softly swore:
"Jeesus! How'd we get in this crazy place?"

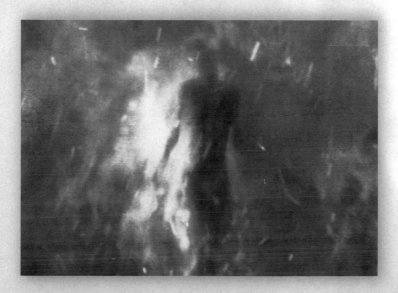

Anne Simon Auger

A Piece of My Heart

ANNE SIMON AUGER AS TOLD TO KEITH WALKER

I remember driving down to Fort Sam Houston with two of the girls who had signed up with me. I can still see us flying down those freeways heading south toward Texas. We felt like we were invincible. We owned the world; we were free, independent. It was really neat.

I remember trying on our combat boots and ponchos and our uniforms; we'd never worn anything so ridiculous in our lives. And we would parade 'round and play games in them and think we were really cool . . . We learned how to march. We thought that was so funny. I remember we had field training. We were given compasses and had to go out and find our way back: we never had so much fun. We got lost twelve times to Tuesday—it didn't matter. We had a little bit of medical training in the field where they would wrap some volunteer up in bandages, put a tag on him saying what was wrong with him, and we had to take care of him. It was totally unrealistic. It was another game. We knew what to do and how to do it from the lesson, but we didn't have any idea of what we were getting ourselves into. We were given weapons training in that they showed us how to fire an M-16, but they wouldn't let us do it. Of course I didn't want to anyway—they were too noisy. They took us through a mock Vietnam village. That was a little scary when they had the punji stick[1] trap come up, but again it was no big deal. And I don't see how the Army could have done any different. I hated them for years for not training me better for Vietnam, but I don't think it could possibly

---

1 **punji stick:** a sharpened bamboo stake concealed in high grass intended to wound the feet and legs of enemy soldiers; often coated with excrement so as to cause an infection

be done. I don't think you can train anybody or teach anybody to experience something that horrible without having them simply live it. . . . Anyway. We got through Fort Sam. It was a lark.

I went to Fort Devons in Massachusetts for six months. I was assigned to the orthopedic ward, and 100 percent of my patients were Vietnam casualties. They were long-term; they had been in Japan before they came to us. I didn't even relate them to Vietnam, and it bothers me now, because they could have been suffering some of the distress that I have, and I didn't recognize it. I know some of them acted really wild and crazy, but I figured it was just because they were kids. While I was there I was dating a psychologist. He was a captain. I'll never forget when I got my orders he was the first one I showed them to, and I was excited. "I'm going to Vietnam!" I told him. He was upset because he was staying there and I was leaving; he thought the man should go. It hadn't dawned on me before that I should be anything but excited. I didn't think to question anything that was going on or to wonder what I was getting myself into. I was just out for experiences at the time, I guess.

So, I remember flying over from Travis. I was the only woman on the plane. There must have been two hundred men on the plane. But everybody was polite and friendly until we got within sight of Vietnam, and then it all just quieted down. Nobody talked; nobody said anything. Everybody had their noses glued to the window. We saw puffs of smoke. The plane took a sudden turn up, and we heard we were being fired on. That was the first time it dawned on me that my life may be in peril. Then I started thinking, "Why would they want to shoot me? I haven't done anything to them." Anyway, we took this steep, real fast dive into Long Binh, and we landed in Vietnam. I remember talking to the nurse in charge of assigning people, and she actually gave me a choice of where I wanted to go. The other nurses with me knew just about where they wanted to go. They all had choices, and I had no idea of one place from another. So I told her to send me wherever she wanted, and she still wouldn't do that. She said, "North or south?" I said, "I don't know." I finally just decided, "Oh hell, send me north. If I'm going to be here I might as well get as close to the North Vietnamese as I can," which is really irrational now, but at the time I didn't know what I was doing. So she assigned me to the 91st Evac.[2]

2 **91st Evac:** a hospital near the front lines; Evac is short for "evacuation"

I was assigned to intensive care and recovery, which is like jumping straight into the fire. I had no preparation for it. I was six months out of nursing school and had worked in a newborn nursery until I joined the Army. It was hectic. It was fast paced. It was depressing. I spent six months there. Two of the incidents that really stand out from those six months: One was when I was working recovery. I had been there a few months, long enough to get numb and build a few walls. This eighteen-year-old GI came into my recovery ward. He had been through surgery. He'd been in an APC[3] that ran over a mine, and I think he was the only survivor. He was just a young kid; I don't even think he had hair on his face yet. And he came out of the anesthesia crying for his mother. I felt so helpless. I was barely older than he was, and he's crying, "Mommy! Mommy! Mommy!" I didn't know what to do. . . . I just held him, and I think that's all I did. It worked, but it was a real experience for me because I certainly wasn't maternal at the time and hadn't thought that that would ever come up. It got me to realize how young and innocent and how naïve these poor kids were. And their choices had been taken away from them.

Then the other incident. We had a sergeant, must have been in his mid forties; he was a drinker, an alcoholic. And he wasn't even involved first line in the war—he was a supply sergeant or something. He came into our intensive care unit with a bleeding ulcer. I remember spending two hours pumping ice water into his stomach, pulling it out, and pumping it back in. We were also pumping blood into him. He died, and he had a family back home, and I thought, "My God, it's bad enough to die over here legitimately"—the gunshot wound—but to die that way seemed like such an awful waste.

The patient that chased me off the ward . . . was a lieutenant named . . . I don't remember his last name—his first name was John. He was twenty-one. He'd gotten married before he came to Vietnam. And he was shot in his face. He absolutely lost his entire face from ear to ear. He had no nose. He was blind. It didn't matter, I guess, because he was absolutely a vegetable. He was alive and breathing: tubes and machines were keeping him alive. . . . I just . . . couldn't handle it. To think of how one instant had affected his life. . . . His wife's life was completely changed, his parents, his friends, me—it affected me too. And all

3 **APC:** armored personnel carrier

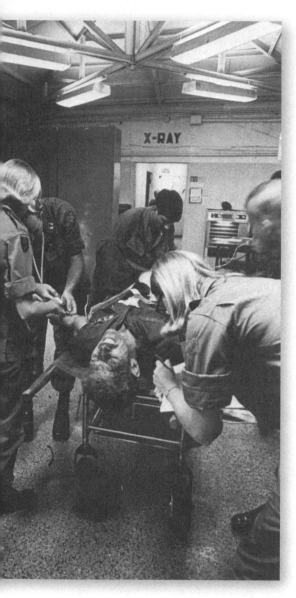

because of one split second. I got to realizing how vulnerable everybody was. And how vulnerable I was. I took care of him for a week. They finally shipped him to Japan, and I never heard from him again. I don't know if he's dead or alive. I don't know how his wife or his family are doing. I don't know how he's doing. It seems like every patient on that ward, when they left, took a piece of me with them. They came in, we would treat them for a few hours or a few days, and then we'd send them off and never hear a word. I had this real need to see one GI who'd survived the war after an injury, because I never saw them—never heard from them again. There was one time in Vietnam when I came so close to writing to my mother and asking her to check around and see if she could find one whole eighteen-year-old. I didn't believe we could have any left. After John left I just couldn't handle it any more. We had too many bodies lying in those beds minus arms and legs, genitals, and faces, and things like that can't be put back together again.

I found I'd built up walls real effectively. I was patient and tender with the GIs. I didn't talk to them a lot because I was afraid to—afraid of losing my cool. I was very professional, but I was distant. I worry sometimes about the way I treated those GIs in intensive care (this was an insight I only got a year ago). . . . I was afraid, because I didn't feel I had done my best with them. Because of the walls I'd put up I didn't listen to them, didn't hear what they might be trying to tell me even just in gestures or whatever. I wasn't open to them because I was so closed to myself.

I got out of ICU.[4] I couldn't handle any more. I asked to be transferred to the Vietnamese ward. Everybody had to do that—spend a rotation in the ward. This is where I found out that war doesn't just hit soldiers, that nobody is safe from war. I can still see this little boy—he was about nine months old. He had both of his legs in a cast and one arm in a cast and his entire abdomen bandaged, because he'd gotten in the way. I delivered a baby for a POW, a stillborn baby. It amazed me that life still went on even in a war. Because it seemed like everything should just stop. We had lots of medical problems too when we weren't too busy with war injuries. I had an eight-year-old girl who died of malnutrition. That's something that we only read about in our textbooks. Her mother brought her in, reluctantly, and she said we had twenty-four hours to cure her. She didn't trust us. If we couldn't cure the kid in twenty-four hours, she was taking her away. She did take her away, and the kid died the day after. To come from a background like I did, where everybody has plenty to eat, a lot of security, and to witness what these kids went through. They were older at the age of four than I was at eighteen. And I'll never forget that look on their faces, that old-man look on those young kids' faces, because they'd lived through so much. That still haunts me today.

The POWs.[5] I took a lot of my frustrations out on them—in innocuous ways. I made one POW chew his aspirin when he wanted something for pain because I didn't think he had any right to complain while there were so many GIs injured . . . just on the next ward. One of the POWs attacked me once—tried to choke me—and I hit back at him. But I think before I even made contact with him, the two MPs[6] were all over him. I never saw him again. We had one twelve-year-old NVA who had killed five GIs. Twelve years old! And he would brag about it to me. He would spit at me. I have never seen such hate. To see the loathing that he had in his eyes was frightening. But at almost the same time, we had a kid on the other side of the ward who was about the same age. He was a scout for the GIs, so he was on "our side." And the GIs just babied him. They thought he was the coolest kid, and he was so tough he scared me.

4 **ICU:** Intensive Care Unit; where those with the most serious injuries are taken to recover

5 **POWs:** Prisoners of War

6 **MPs:** military policemen

One of my most traumatic and long-lasting experiences happened to me while working the POW ward. An NVA was admitted with gunshot wounds he got during an ambush on a platoon of GIs. This POW was personally responsible for the deaths of six of those GIs. When he was wheeled into my ward, something snapped. I was overwhelmed with uncontrollable feelings of hate and rage. I couldn't go near this guy because I knew, without any doubt, that if I touched him I would kill him. I was shaking from trying to keep my hands off his neck. This scared me to death, and for twelve years after I was scared of experiencing it again. I discovered that I was capable of killing and of violently hating another human being. I had been raised to be a loving and giving person. As a nurse, I had vowed to help *all* who need it. As a human being I should love my brother, whoever he was. I was forced to confront a side of myself I never dreamed existed before.

After four months on the Vietnamese ward, I asked to be transferred again. So I was put on the GI medical ward. That was more depressing than the first two wards I'd been on. Mostly because the people that I had labeled as cop-outs were on that ward. The drug abusers, the alcoholics, the guys in there with malaria—because rather than go out in the field they would not take their malaria pills so they could come down with malaria. I was really very unsympathetic to them. I didn't try to understand them. After so many months of taking care of "legitimate" injuries, I couldn't handle that. I just figured, "Hell, even I can take this. Why can't you? You're supposed to be braver and stronger than I am, and somehow I'm managing."

We were shelled monthly, at least monthly. The closest call we had was when I was on the medical ward. I remember mortars were falling all around us. I had just gotten my sixty patients under their mattresses, and I dove under a bed myself, finally, and then this GI next to me says, "Hey, you forgot . . ." whatever his name was, and sure enough—he was one of our drug ODs—he was lying on top of his bed singing. I had to get out, crawl over to him, pull him out of bed, and put the mattress over him. I remember screaming at him. I was so mad at him for making me take any more chances. This happened the same day that my sister got married. In fact it was almost the same hour, and I thought, "My God, they're partying, and here I am." We had a sapper attack too when I was on that ward. That's when somebody infiltrates our perimeter. There's a certain siren that goes off. At the time, my corpsman on the ward was a conscientious objector, so he wouldn't handle any firearms. I remember I had to grab the M-16 and stand guard after I had locked the doors. I didn't even know how to fire the damn thing! I finally had to haul one of my patients—he was a lieutenant, I remember—out of bed and had him stand with me in case the gun needed to be fired. Once again, I had the preconception that women were supposed to be taken care of, and it seemed like I was doing all the taking care of.

A lot more happened; I just don't like pulling it out. . . . It's behind me now, and I think what became of me is more important anyway.

I remember on the plane home I held my breath until we were probably a thousand miles from Vietnam, because I was so afraid that something would happen and we'd have to go back. We landed at Sea Tac.[7] I remember getting a hotel room and calling my parents, because they wanted to come out from Michigan to meet me. I ended up going back to the airport to meet them on *my* way home from Vietnam. They wanted to stay for two days in Seattle and sightsee. I can vividly see me sitting on this tour bus, looking out the window at nothing. Feeling up in the air, lost, disoriented. I was still back there. I didn't smile much. They thought I was angry. Well, they didn't know. They were trying to act like things were just the same as always—that a year hadn't gone by and that I hadn't gone anywhere. They were doing that to relax me. . . . I'm sure they were hurting too. I jumped at any noise. I looked at people walking the streets, and there wasn't even fear in their eyes. All I could think was, "If you only knew . . . you wouldn't be so damned complacent." I didn't even feel like going home. I wish I could have gone somewhere for a while—just to be by myself. I was pushed right back into everyday living, when I was still so far away from it and so disjointed that I couldn't possibly fit in. Everybody tried to ignore where I'd been. I guess some people did ask me about Vietnam, and I would say things like "It was okay." Or "Actually it was the pits." That's all I said for ten years. ◌

---

7 **Sea Tac:** Seattle Tacoma International Airport

Responding to Cluster Two

What Was the War Experience?

Thinking Skill ANALYZING

1. **Tone** is a writer's attitude toward the subject he or she is writing about. For example, a writer might take a playful, somber, or sarcastic attitude toward a topic. **Analyze** the tone of "I-Feel-Like-I'm-Fixin'-To-Die Rag" and "The Ballad of the Green Berets."

2. According to Alex Forman in "Hippies," what type of world did the hippies hope to create?

3. How does Rico's Mexican heritage affect his decisions in the story "Village"?

4. What do the poems "Farmer Nguyen" and "A Nun in Ninh Hoa" tell you about Vietnamese attitudes toward the war?

5. Why does the narrator of "A Piece of My Heart" build up walls?

Writing Activity: Spinning the News

The conflict in Vietnam was the first war that Americans could watch from the comfort of their living rooms. In fact, the conflict sparked a media war between hawks (those in favor of military action) and doves (those in favor of peaceful solutions). Headlines and news reports were the weapons in this war of words and images. For example, doves would emphasize the cost of the war by showing casualties and destruction. Hawks, on the other hand, tended to emphasize American military victories.

Analyze the incidents in the list below, select three to five of them, and then write two headlines for each. One headline should emphasize the dove perspective; one should emphasize the hawk point of view.

• U.S. Navy destroyer *Maddox* said to be attacked by North Vietnamese PT boats
• Hippies setting up a free store and a commune in San Francisco
• Rico shooting Sergeant Keever to prevent a village from being destroyed
• Hugh Thompson's decision to report the massacre at My Lai.

You might use the following headlines as models. Notice how each one puts a different spin on a familiar tale.

Wolf Destroys Homes, Two Pigs Injured
Cleanup of Pig Sties a Success, Wolf Says

A Strong Headline
• is short.
• highlights the main topic or issue of the story.
• uses strong action verbs (strikes, upholds, defends).
• uses the present tense.

CLUSTER THREE

What Was Happening Back Home?
Thinking Skill   GENERALIZING

San Fransisco

**(Be Sure to Wear Some
Flowers in Your Hair)**

JOHN PHILLIPS

If you're going to San Francisco,
Be sure to wear some flowers in your hair.
If you're going to San Francisco,
You're gonna meet some gentle people there.

For those who come to San Francisco,
Summer time will be a loving there.
In the streets of San Francisco
Gentle People wear flowers in their hair.

All cross the nation
Such a strange vibration.
People in motion
There is a whole generation
With a new explanation.
People in motion,
People in motion.

For those who come to San Francisco,
Be sure to wear some flowers in your hair.
If you come to San Francisco.
Summer time will be a loving there.
If you come to San Francisco,
Summer time will be a loving there.

Law and Order Chicago Style

DONALD KAUL

In the Summer of 1968, nearly ten thousand war protesters tried to enter the Democratic National Convention in downtown Chicago. They were denied entry because they were not on the approved roster of speakers. The protesters, many with long hair, took to hanging out in Grant Park chanting anti-war slogans. Chicago police turned brutal in their efforts to restrain the protesters—often beating and gassing innocent bystanders and news reporters. Live television cameras were rolling as protesters and police clashed. Americans watched in disbelief as protesters chanted "The whole world is watching!" Des Moines Register *columnist Donald Kaul was one of many who saw the brutality firsthand.*

I got my first real taste of Law and Order in Chicago last week, and I must say that, in retrospect, it was no worse than being tarred and feathered and ridden out of town on a rail.

Admittedly, Mayor Daley had a problem. Four or five thousand Yippies or hippies descended upon the city with the avowed intention of disrupting the business of the Democratic National Convention.

I have never been a great fan of the hippies and I was not particularly fond of these. They chanted obscenities. They waved Viet Cong flags. They littered the public parks.

Clearly they could not be allowed to have their way with the town, but Daley's response to the situation was altogether incredible. He turned Chicago into a police state—literally.

Police and anti-war demonstrators clash during the 1968 Democratic Convention in Chicago.

In most cases, the cops outnumbered the hippies by at least two to one, so that whenever the cops went headhunting, which was often, there simply weren't enough hippies to go around.

Lacking sufficient hippies, the cops made do with whatever was available—reporters, delegates, shop girls, lovers on strolls and Pulitzer Prize-winning cartoonists.

▲   ▲   ▲

On the night before the convention I followed some raucous hippies down Michigan Avenue to the Chicago River where they were stopped by a police line. At this point, there were about 100 hippies, 50 cops.

The cops began to herd the demonstrators into the blind corner in front of the Wrigley Building when a scruffy, barefooted kid in a helmet yelled out: "Don't let them get you in there. It's a death trap."

I thought that overstatement pretty funny and was still chuckling about it when four buses pulled up to within 10 feet of where I was standing.

"That's strange," I said to myself, "I thought the buses were on strike."

In the next two seconds 150 cops piled out of those buses, all with helmets, all with clubs—150 cops and I was afraid of every one of them.

As I sprinted down the street yelling "Press! Press!" I decided to get a haircut the next day. Chicago was not a good place to be mistaken for a hippie in a suit and tie, was the way I figured it.

▲   ▲   ▲

So the next day I got the haircut and went to Lincoln Park to watch the police clear it of its hippie squatters.

There must have been a thousand police there.

They warned the snarling, bottle-throwing hippies to leave the park and, upon being ignored, hit them with tear gas and sent in 200 cops to beat them up.

As the first wave of police advanced, their comrades standing in reserve began yelling: "Kill! Kill! Kill!" I began to have second thoughts about the deathtrap remarks.

I managed to stay out of trouble throughout the long and bloody evening and on my way back to my hotel I was stopped by a police officer.

"Where do you think you're going, buddy?" he said. I showed my press credentials.

"Oh, one of the hippie press, eh?" he said. Right there I knew I hadn't gotten my hair cut short enough. He seemed about to bash me when two of his fellow police officers stopped him and told me to get the hell out of there. I got the hell out of there.

▲   ▲   ▲

Other well-known hippie elements—John McCormally, editor of the *Burlington Hawk-Eye,* and The *Register's* cartoonist, Frank Miller—were tear-gassed.

Miller had a particularly rough convention. He was knocked down by a policeman during a hippie demonstration early in the week, he was tear-gassed and he was harassed.

One day he was sitting in the Conrad Hilton coffee shop, staring abstractedly into space as is his habit, when a cop walked over and said: "What are you staring at us for?"

Miller denied that he was and produced his credentials, which happened to be those of a news photographer.

"Where's your camera?"

"In my hotel room," Miller answered, not wanting to go into a lengthy explanation.

"If you know what's good for you, you'll keep it there," the cop said, and walked away. ❧

Like a Rolling Stone

BEN FONG-TORRES

The 1960s was the era of the "generation gap"—parents no longer seemed to understand their long-haired, peace-loving children. Ben Fong-Torres not only faced the "generation gap," he also faced a cultural gap. When Ben began reporting for the new magazine Rolling Stone, *the gap between him and his parents widened even further.*

Unshackled from the corporate world, I dressed more casually than I even had in college. There, taking my role as an editor too seriously, I often showed up at the newspaper office in a white shirt and narrow tie. With my horn-rimmed glasses and short hair, I looked like some engineering student who'd stumbled into the wrong place.

Now, I took to blue work shirts and jeans. I switched to rimless glasses. I grew a moustache and I let my hair grow, leaving it unwashed for days at a time.

Still, like my siblings, I would manage to make my way over to Hayward and to the Bamboo Hut to work a few hours or an entire day on the occasional weekend. With [sister] Shirley married and in Texas, [brother] Burton took over most of the chores, while [brother] Barry and I made guest appearances.

When I showed up one Sunday that summer, my parents were not happy to see me. They did not mince words, and as soon as my mother saw me, she cried out: *"Ai-ya! Nay kawyeong!"* This has no direct English translation, but roughly meant, "You look like that?"

"Why so long?" she asked, indicating my hair and looking ashamed for me. "It looks not good." She didn't press the issue, but when she went into the kitchen, she told my father, and he came out to the dining room for a look.

It was the middle of the afternoon, and there were no customers.

"You look like a *girl*," he snapped.

That's all it took. I turned, gave poor Burton a pat on the shoulder—he'd be working alone again—and drove back to San Francisco.

A few days later, Barry heard about the blowup and called. He, too, had grown a moustache, but he kept his hair at early Beatles length, with sideburns. He was a probation officer and subject to office policies.

"You should tell them it's a job requirement," he said, laughing.

"How do you say 'job requirement' in Chinese?" I asked. It was a rhetorical question. In Chinese, there are no requirements. You just showed up and worked.

"I know," said Barry. "I'll bring them some pictures of some *real* freaks. That should calm them down."

▲　▲　▲

When I next visited home for my mother's birthday in August, the subject of hair-length was left undiscussed. But, then, so was almost every subject. We were incapable of talking about politics, the war, civil rights, or what young people were thinking. My parents, as far as I knew, didn't care. Their only concern was that their children would not become hippies.

When I joined *Rolling Stone*, I told them only that I was working at a newspaper in San Francisco that covered music. There was no easy way—and no point, really—telling them more. My parents tended to judge people on surface appearances. That's how they had treated Shirley's dates; how they responded to various friends of ours; and why Barry and I rarely talked about our dates. When Barry mentioned that he liked Kate, and that she was not Chinese, Mom had told him, "Please, don't. Sarah already upset us so much."

They meant well. Sure, they had their own concerns about *seet-meen*, the dreaded loss of face; they wanted us to be more Chinese, even if it meant being less American. But they were also concerned for us. They, too, knew about racism and knew that life would be easier for their sons and daughters if they weren't involved in interracial marriages.

I wished I could have engaged them in a real conversation about my feelings. I understand your concerns, I would have said. But I can't let your worries about how people in Chinatown look at you dictate how I live my life.

Here I am, in a profession few, if any, Asians have cracked, and race had absolutely nothing to do with my getting the job. That was true of my jobs at the phone company magazine, at the radio station, and in college.

Here I am, an editor at a magazine chronicling not only music but the massive social and cultural revolutions that are irrevocably changing our world. At the heart of the movement is an ideal, of a more just and equal society in which one recognizes differences in cultures, but doesn't discriminate because of those differences.

And here I am, writing about some of the most creative forces of our time, many of them rhythm and blues artists I have loved since first turning on Top 40 radio ten years ago.

This is who I am, and you're asking that I go out with only Chinese? I'm sorry, but I can't do that. And it's not because I need to rebel against you, to do the opposite of what you want. In an ideal world, I would love a woman who happened to be Chinese, and we'd all be happy. In reality, the women I'm seeing are people you wouldn't want to meet. They're good women, too. It's just too bad they've got that one thing wrong with them.

Once, I used the pages of *East West* [a weekly English-language tabloid for the city's Chinese community] to tear into my fellow Chinese—specifically, Chinese a generation older than me—for their racist ways. Somewhere in America, there were Chinese kids who did kowtow to their parents in the matters of professions and relationships. That kind of submission, I said, fostered perpetual racism and other biases. That was the kind of thinking, I wrote, that had to be wiped out "among people of all colors."

Seeing my raw anger in print, I was relieved that my parents couldn't read English. Barry could, and sent me a note from Hawaii, where he was spending a weekend with Kate. "Continue socking it to them," he said. ❧

Woodstock Nation

Marc Aronson

Bethel, New York, August 15, 1969

Whether they drove, took buses, or hitched rides to Max Yasgur's farm, the hundreds of thousands of rock fans gathering for the Woodstock Music and Art Fair had to hike the last stretch. Like campers on a late summer adventure, they made their way through the dark woods, along a narrow path onward, ever onward, toward the music. Running, singing songs, exchanging rumors—the festival was free, the fence around the grounds was down—the army of young people rushed on. The marchers were a parade of hippie fashion: thin long-haired men, women in halter tops or long peasant dresses, many wearing beads and headbands and tie-dye. Along the path they saw radicalized friends and familiar-looking strangers from around the country, feeling for the first time the power of their numbers. Posters, programs and tickets promised "three days of peace & music," but the excited fans wanted more than that. As Woodstock Nation, the young people who slogged through the mud, woke up to the music, and skinny-dipped in the Catskills lakes embodied the dream of transforming America.

To this day, whether as nostalgia or satire, Woodstock remains the symbol of the peace-and-love sixties. Breakfast was provided by a West Coast commune, the Hog Farm; their good works were announced by Wavy Gravy, an archetypical laid-back hippie. If enough drugs, rock, sex, and granola could change the children of driven, materialistic parents

Janis Joplin

into Zen saints, this was the moment. The poster for the guru Maher Baba with his mantra "Don't worry, be happy," the tribal groupings gathered in tepees, geodesic domes, and under the canopy of trees, the anthems of the rock stars announced that a new age was at hand.

In their backpacks the wide-eyed fans carried battered paperbacks that confirmed their sense that they were a generation with a special destiny. Utopian fantasies such as Robert Rimmer's *The Harrar Experiment* and science fiction novels such as Robert Heinlein's *Stranger in a Strange Land*, with their own vision of new, open lifestyles, competed for space with *The Lord of the Rings* trilogy of J.R.R. Tolkien. The festival grounds even resembled Middle-earth. Away from the cities everything had to be made, cooked, and set up by hand. Between the rain-drenched colorful clothes and the long hair, people began to look more like medieval hobbits than modern humans. And then there was the great feeling in the air. Everyone sensed that a great quest had begun, and that every moment was significant. If outside, elsewhere, was great evil, that was expected in epic times. In these young people lay power. If they looked bedraggled and humble, so did many heroes when their journeys began. And, like mythic heroes, they made their own rules.

Everything that was hidden, illegal, and uncommon in the rest of America was public, condoned, displayed for all to see at Woodstock. To one side of a hand-lettered sign with prices for drugs a cobbler offered homemade sandals, while on the other, a half-dressed hippie family played songs and games well into the night. To some of the people there, as to the media covering the event, the filmmakers and sound engineers who recorded it, and the millions around the world who paid to listen to it or to see it on-screen, this was the triumph of freedom. A generation that would not put up with old lies, hypocrisy, and boredom was demonstrating its alternative vision of how people could live and love. Woodstock was idealistic young America triumphant. It was the theme park of the avant-garde generation. ∾

Jimi Hendrix

Woodstock:
The Oral History

Irwin Unger

Rick Gavras: We all jumped in the car. . . . I was supposed to meet my girlfriend. . . . I was supposed to meet her at Woodstock and, of course, little did we know that there was going to be a few hundred thousand people there. So I never did meet her. I suppose we thought there was some sort of front gate or something of that sort. . . . When I got there, it was just, well, there was a lot of land. I don't know how many acres it was, but there was no front entrance at that point. I think everybody was pretty much being allowed just to go in. It was just kind of like a long field and just people sort of en masse kind of converging on the spot, and I realized right away I wasn't going to meet Mimi.

Alan Green: There was no idea of how big the thing could possibly be. . . . So we packed up a little bit of food, some dope, a jacket—once again, there was no planning at all, unlike a lot of people who seemed to arrive with all sorts of provisions. . . . I think we started out around noon and picked up someone hitchhiking, and as we started getting closer . . . up the Thruway . . . there were people all of a sudden appearing with signs: WOODSTOCK. And as it got closer, it was really obvious that something was happening, and there was this—it was sort of weird. . . .

Rick Gavras: It was overwhelming because there were so many people. It was like something kind of colossal. There was a stage. And the stage from where I was for the first couple of days was real far away because I was way, way in back. I was busy kind of strolling all over the place. And I never really got up close to the stage until the third day, the very last day.

I pretty much stayed with my friends most of the time, or at least a couple of them. And, of course, we were all taking LSD twenty-four hours a day and smoking twenty-four hours a day, which I guess most people were doing. And so everything was very surreal.

Diana Warshawsky: It wasn't ever an out-of-control situation. I know they had emergency stands . . . in case somebody was flipping out or sick or hurt or anything, and it was a very peaceful group of people. People were just happy, you know, getting stoned and just being happy to be there. But I found it very unnerving to be with this many people inside a barbed wire. And there was a helicopter flying over . . . I felt like I was trapped. . . . I was having a good time because of, you know, being with my friends, the person I was with, and I remember, in terms of music, I have almost no recollection of the music except that the only performer that I remember is Richie Havens. I remember him and I remember really liking that, but that's it. I don't know who else performed that night. Actually, I'd be curious to know.

I do remember that when the music was over for that evening, we sort of trudged down a road and found a relatively hospitable place to unroll sleeping bags off the side of the road, and slept that night. . . . I wanted to leave the next morning. And so we ended up hitchhiking out of the area back into New York City. . . .

Joseph Coakley: I remember how incredibly crowded it was. I can remember putting my hand somewhere and then not being able to move it for two hours. . . . It was just incredibly cramped. . . .

I remember it rained that night. I can remember we were hungry, and there were some concession stands at the top of the bowl that for all intents and purposes were the only places I knew of to eat, and these political people, you know, that were wandering around the area—you didn't see them or whatever, but I understand that some of the concessions got torched that night due to their high prices or whatever, which further burdened the whole problem of what to eat. But as I remember waking up the next morning, it was a sea of mud. That bowl was just incredible. Everybody was cold and wet. Just a very unpleasant camping experience out there in the mud bowl. But as I remember, the music stopped Friday night; I don't think they played all night Friday night. I don't remember if they did or not.

Rick Gavras: As far as the music goes, what I remember mostly was they had two stages set up on the sides of the main stage. I remember one night of the main stage real vividly, but most of my memories of music were on the side stages. And there was where you could kind of lay in the grass, and it wasn't real crowded. The Grateful Dead played there a lot. That was cool. They were really into relating with the people. I remember seeing them a lot and sitting on the stage and how wonderful they were at that time. And the music I remember the most out of everything was on one stage, and that was basically the people that stand out mostly in my mind: Santana and Sly and the Family Stone. I think they all played on one night. Janis Joplin. That was kind of the most connected night I had. I was just totally enveloped in the music. . . . The music was real important but there was just so much stuff going on. . . .

I think maybe a lot of it had to do with kind of maintaining a sense of reality for me, especially when you're tripping twenty-four hours a day. A lot of stuff sure appeared weird. Maybe a lot of that had to do with how people looked. . . . Just seeing so many strange, strangely adorned people and all the costumes and just the intensity of how the people were relating to each other in a lot of ways. Not so much through speaking and everything, but just through the experience and the being there and people kind of smiling and dancing. People were giving away drugs, LSD and stuff like that. . . . ∞

Editor's Note:

In the summer of 1999, promoters tried to re-enact the Woodstock festival at a former U.S. Air Force base in Rome, N.Y. But the magic was gone. In place of rock 'n' roll legends Janis Joplin, Jefferson Airplane, and Jimi Hendrix, bands such as Korn, the Dave Matthews Band, Limp Bizkit, and the Brian Setzer Orchestra took the stage. Price gouging for food and water angered many of the 200,000 concertgoers. On Sunday night, tensions exploded. After the Red Hot Chili Peppers played, "peace candles" were used to set a car on fire. Up to 500 angry youths set raging bonfires alight on sound equipment. Seven hundred police in full riot gear were called in to stop the violence.

State of Emergency at
"The People's Republic of Berkeley"

TOM HAYDEN

The bloodiest 1969 confrontation, a precursor of Kent State and
Jackson State one year later, took place over "People's Park," an acre of
neglected vacant land belonging to the university just south of campus
and one block from Telegraph.[1] The university, it was believed, was quietly planning to transform the lot into a colorless mall, hoping to pressure
away the legions of hippies, teenage runaways, sidewalk jewelers, and

1 **Telegraph:** a street near the campus of the University of California
at Berkeley

tarot readers, not to mention revolutionary leafleteers who dominated the once-respectable south-campus area. Instead one day, a group of quite gentle street people took up shovels and began making a community park out of the littered and unused lot. Their act caught on, and over several weekends a growing number labored, hammered, and planted grass until a charming, green, little gathering place came into existence, with plenty of benches for relaxing, and swings and building blocks for kids. Tambourines and flutes played into the night as the builders took pride in their creation. Stew Albert and Judy Clavir, two of the most political Yippies, drew me into this creation of "turf." I helped a little with the manual labor, enjoying this refreshing respite from the usual wars with the system. Many political radicals viewed the park project as a hippie cop-out from serious revolutionary work, and a lively debate developed over where the life-style component fit into one's agenda. This inquiry was cut short rather quickly, however, since the university looked with growing distress at this unauthorized urban beautification project. They would not tolerate it, and we would not abandon the gardens and saplings just planted. To head off an irrational confrontation, several city officials and faculty leaders proposed negotiations with the university for a change of ownership of the $1.3 million property. The debate over the park drew such national figures as General William Dean, a Korean War commander who pushed a hard line, and Thomas Hoving, director of New York's Metropolitan Museum of Art, who urged creation of the new park. Meanwhile, a handful of local activists posted themselves in the park every night, sensing possible trouble.

With no warning, hard-line elements decided to move against the park, on the night of May 14. Captain Charles Plummer pulled his battle-ready Berkeley police together for a pep talk, declaring that they were "the last stronghold against the Commies, and today we are going to crush them." Just before dawn, Berkeley police officers, backed by a helicopter and 250 highway patrolmen, marched into the park, forcing out the young people maintaining the watch. At five A.M., about fifty construction workers, protected by the police, erected an eight-foot-high chain link fence all the way around the block containing the park. Like many Berkeley activists, I was awakened early in the morning with phone calls recounting what happened. By eight A.M., many were standing in cold disbelief around the fence being spiked into the park they had built. Inside the fence, heavily protected Berkeley police lounged and laughed on the children's swings. According to the press, the university explained that the fence was installed "to make sure that the land was recognized as University property."

By noon, at least five thousand people were massed in nearby Sproul Plaza to protest the destruction of the park. Though an exact plan was never discussed, it was clear that the angered crowd would tear the fence down if they reached it. I was scheduled to speak on the steps of Sproul Hall and was wondering what to advise while I listened to student body president Dan Siegel. Dan called out something about the need to "take back the park"—and was drowned out by the impatient throng, who turned his phrase into a chant, and before our eyes began moving in a giant sea toward Telegraph Avenue and the three short blocks to the location of the park. Ahead of them, we could see thick lines of police with gas masks already on. They also held tear-gas launchers and shotguns. As the crowd walked and trotted toward their positions, the police began wafting canisters of gas, trailing a wisp of white smoke, at the front line. The marchers held, covering their eyes, and a few ran forward to pick up the hot canisters and hurl them back toward the police.

From this initial stand-off, there began seventeen consecutive days of street fighting, the longest such battle in American history, finally ending in a solemn and nonviolent march to the park fence by almost thirty thousand people. During those days, scenes of the Vietnam War were replayed on a college campus for the first time. The Alameda county sheriffs carried shotguns loaded, not only with birdshot but with deadly double-O buckshot, never before used against students. About 150 demonstrators were shot and wounded, many in the back. Seventy people were treated for gunshot wounds at local hospitals.

On May 15, the day the fence went up and we marched down Telegraph Avenue, a Berkeley freshman named Steve Carr climbed on the roof of an apartment building overlooking the skirmishes. Now a loan officer at Citibank in San Francisco, he remembered being a Naval ROTC student who was "curious about what was going on." He wanted to get above the tear gas, so he sat on a rooftop and watched. The sheriffs' response to the march had been immediate; they started opening fire on people. But then there was a lull, Carr recalled. A car was burning, but the avenue had quieted down. I was on the avenue, where debris, rocks, and overturned trash cans reflected a growing war zone. I was choking from the gas and yelling that people should move off the avenue, where they were easy targets. The police looked like armed and swaggering astronauts, slowly swiveling in the avenue with weapons pointed only a few feet away. Then Carr saw someone who'd thrown a brick from the rooftop twenty minutes earlier. "I turned and told him not to do it again. Then I felt a tremendous concussion, like a tear-gas canister." The sheriffs had spun and fired across four rooftops. Carr was hit with 125 pieces of birdshot; one pellet was less than a millimeter from his eye; another was lodged against his carotid artery. The individual sitting next to him, Alan Blanchard, was not lucky enough to have turned his head and was instantly blinded. Two roofs over, a twenty-five-year-old carpenter named James Rector was wounded and bleeding. All three waited over forty-five minutes in an apartment before being taken to the hospital, where Rector died twenty-four hours later.

On the day following Rector's death, a funeral march and vigil was met by a National Guard helicopter, which dropped white clouds of misty CS gas[2] over Sproul Plaza. Several hundred faculty members started to boycott the university the next day, calling for the chancellor's resignation and charging that the campus was becoming an "experimental laboratory for the National Guard." The student paper demanded the closing of the university as "not safe for human beings."

On the other hand, Major General Glenn Ames, commander of the state National Guard, defended the helicopter drop of CS gas as "perfectly logical." Ronald Reagan had not yet made his famous statement—"If the students want a bloodbath, let's get it over with"—but the murderous precedent was established. (Reagan's bloodbath comment was made to the Council of California Growers on April 7, 1970—one month before Kent State.)

Steve Carr, whose father was a military officer, spent three days in an intensive care unit at Oak Knoll Naval Hospital, where an American soldier wounded in Vietnam slowly died next to him. He watched the rest of the Berkeley events on television among the war-wounded in the hospital and was released ten days later. He testified at a coroner's inquest and trial that he thought the policies of Ed Meese and the county sheriffs were an "extreme reaction." I went to visit Alan Blanchard shortly after he was shot, fighting off feelings of responsibility for what had happened to him. He was a blond, long-haired young man in his mid-twenties, an aspiring artist. But now he was uncomfortably rotating his head to locate me, trying to adjust to his sudden deprivation. Though still in shock at the sudden and random nature of his loss, he moved me by his acceptance of the life he now faced. I went away still feeling guilty. ∾

2 **CS gas:** tear gas

Cambodia

April 30, 1970

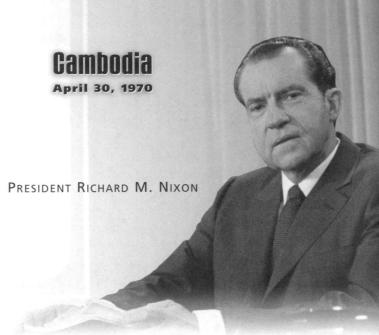

PRESIDENT RICHARD M. NIXON

Good evening my fellow Americans:

Ten days ago, in my report to the Nation on Vietnam, I announced a decision to withdraw an additional 150,000 Americans from Vietnam over the next year. I said then that I was making that decision despite our concern over increased enemy activity in Laos, Cambodia, and in South Vietnam.

At that time, I warned that if I concluded that increased enemy activity in any of these areas endangered lives of Americans remaining in Vietnam, I would not hesitate to take strong and effective measures.

Despite that warning, North Vietnam has increased its military aggression in all these areas, and particularly in Cambodia. After full consultation with the National Security Council, Ambassador Bunker, General Abrams, and my other advisors, I have concluded that the actions of the enemy in the last 10 days clearly endanger the lives of Americans who are in Vietnam now and would constitute an unacceptable risk to those who will be there after withdrawal of another 150,000.

To protect our men who are in Vietnam and to guarantee the continued success of our withdrawal and Vietnamization programs, I have concluded that the time has come for action.

Tonight, I shall describe the actions of the enemy, the actions I have ordered to deal with that situation, and the reasons for my decision.

Cambodia, a small country of 7 million people, has been a neutral nation since the Geneva agreement of 1954, an agreement, incidentally, which was signed by the Government of North Vietnam. American policy since then has been to scrupulously respect the neutrality of the Cambodian people.

North Vietnam, however, has not respected that neutrality. For the past 5 years as indicated on this map that you see here North Vietnam has occupied military sanctuaries all along the Cambodian frontier with South Vietnam. Some of these extend up to 20 miles into Cambodia. . . . In cooperation with the armed forces of South Vietnam, attacks are being launched this week to clean out major enemy sanctuaries on the Cambodian Vietnam border.

A major responsibility for the ground operations is being assumed by South Vietnamese forces. . . .

There is one area, however, immediately above Parrot's Beak, where I have concluded that a combined American and South Vietnamese operation is necessary.

Tonight, American and South Vietnamese units will attack the headquarters for the entire Communist military operation in South Vietnam. This key control center has been occupied by the North Vietnamese and Vietcong for 5 years in blatant violation of Cambodia's neutrality.

We take this action not for the purpose of expanding the war into Cambodia but for the purpose of ending the war in Vietnam and winning the just peace we all desire. We have made, we will continue to make, every possible effort to end this war through negotiation at the conference table rather than through more fighting on the battlefield. . . .

The action that I have announced tonight puts the leaders of North Vietnam on notice that we will be patient in working for peace, we will be conciliatory at the conference table, but we will not be humiliated. We will not be defeated. We will not allow American men by the thousands to be killed by an enemy from privileged sanctuaries. . . .

I have rejected all political considerations in making this decision. . . . Whether my party gains in November[1] is nothing compared to the lives of 400,000 brave Americans fighting for our country and for the cause of peace and freedom in Vietnam. Whether I may be a one-term President is insignificant compared to whether, by our failure to act in this crisis, the United States proves itself to be unworthy to lead the forces of freedom in this critical period in world history. I would rather be a one-term President and do what I believe is right than to be a two-term President at the cost of seeing America become a second rate power and to see this Nation accept the first defeat in its proud 190-year history. . . . ❧

1 **whether my party gains in November:** a reference to congressional elections to occur in November 1970

The Kent State Tragedy

ROGER BARR

President Nixon's expansion of the war into Cambodia on April 30, 1970, caused a national outburst of violent protests. One such protest on May 1 resulted in a confrontation between National Guardsmen and students at Kent State University in Ohio.

The campus had been the scene of a weekend of protests. The ROTC headquarters had been burned down on Saturday evening, May 2. The city's mayor, LeRoy Satrom, had asked Ohio governor James Rhodes to send National Guard troops to restore order. The guard arrived late that night and took up positions on campus. On Sunday, May 3, the guardsmen broke up a student rally with bayonets.

On Monday, May 4, the students reassembled at noon on the campus commons to hold a rally. The students were told that the assembly was unlawful and were ordered to disperse. The students were incensed. They seemed to switch their attention from the war to the fact that the National Guard was on their campus. The students threw rocks at the guardsmen, and the guardsmen fired tear gas into the crowds. The guardsmen then went through the commons and returned to their original positions at 12:24 p.m. Suddenly, according to witnesses, the guardsmen turned and started firing into the crowd. Thirteen seconds later, the shooting stopped. Four students lay dead or dying, and nine more were wounded.

The deaths of the four students rocked America and sparked even more protests. Students went on strike on hundreds of campuses across the nation. Many campuses were closed for the rest of the school year. More than seventy-five thousand protesters marched on Washington, D.C., on May 9.

To an ever-increasing number of Americans, the deaths at Kent State symbolized what was wrong with U.S. involvement in Vietnam. These deaths were unnecessary and senseless. The tragedy somehow proved that everything protesters had been saying about their government was right. ∾

Mary Ann Vecchio kneels by the body of Kent State student Jeffrey Miller.

Born on the Fourth of July

RON KOVIC

I was in Vietnam when I first heard about the thousands of people protesting the war in the streets of America. I didn't want to believe it at first—people protesting against *us* when we were putting our lives on the line for our country. The men in my outfit used to talk about it a lot. How could they do this to us? Many of us would not be coming back and many others would be wounded or maimed. We swore they would pay, the hippies and draftcard burners. They would pay if we ever ran into them.

But the hospital had changed all that. It was the end of whatever belief I'd still had in what I'd done in Vietnam. Now I wanted to know what I had lost my legs for, why I and the others had gone at all. But it was still very hard for me to think of speaking out against the war, to think of joining those I'd once called traitors.

I settled into my apartment again and went back to classes at the university. It was the spring of 1970. I still wore a tie and sweater every day to school and had a short haircut. I was very sensitive to people looking at me in the wheelchair. I buried myself in my books, cutting myself off from the other students. It was as if they threatened me—particularly the activists, the radicals.

I was sitting alone in my apartment listening to the radio when I first heard the news about Kent State. Four students had just been shot in a demonstration against the invasion of Cambodia. For a moment there was a shock through my body. I felt like crying. The last time I had felt that way was the day Kennedy was killed. I remember saying to myself, The whole thing is coming down now. I wheeled out to my car. I didn't know where I was going but I had to find other people who felt the way I did. I drove down the street to the university. Students were congregating in small groups all over the place. The campus looked as if it were going to explode. Banners were going up and monitors with red armbands were walking up and down handing out leaflets. There was going to be a march and demonstration. I thought carefully for a moment or two, then decided to participate, driving my car past the hundreds of students marching down to the big parking lot where the rally was to be held. I honked my horn in support but I was still feeling a little hesitant. I stayed in my car all during the rally, listening intently to each speaker and cheering and shouting with the crowd. I was still acting like an observer. The last speaker was a woman who said there would be a huge rally in Washington that Saturday and that it was hoped that everyone would make it down. I decided I would go.

That night I called my cousin Ginny's husband Skip. He used to come and visit me at the hospital when I first came back and after I got out we became good friends. Sometimes we'd stay up all night at his house playing cards and talking about Vietnam and what had happened to me. Skip's views were very different from mine back then. He was against the war. And each time I left his house to go home, he'd give me books to read—books about the black people and poor people of the country. I laughed at him at first and didn't take the books too seriously, but it was lonely in my room and soon I began to read. And before long, every time I went to his house I asked for more books. Skip seemed surprised when I asked him to go to the rally with me but he said yes, and early Saturday morning we left for Washington.

▲ ▲ ▲

The New Jersey Turnpike was packed with cars painted with flags and signs, and everywhere there were people hitching, holding up big cardboard peace symbols. You didn't have to ask where anyone was going. We were all going to the same place. Washington was a madhouse with buses and trucks and cars coming in from all directions.

We got a parking space and I gave up my tie and sweater for no shirt and a big red bandana around my head. Skip pushed the wheelchair for what seemed a mile or so. We could feel the tremendous tension. People were handing out leaflets reminding everyone that this was a nonviolent demonstration, and that no purpose would be served in violent confrontation. I remember feeling a little scared, the way I did before a

firefight. After reading the leaflet I felt content that no one was going to get hurt.

Skip and I moved as close to the speakers' platform as we could and Skip lifted me out of my chair and laid me on my cushion. People were streaming into the Ellipse from all around us—an army of everyday people. There was a guy with a stereo tape deck blasting out music, and dogs running after Frisbees on the lawn. The Hari Krishna people started to dance and the whole thing seemed like a weird carnival. But there was a warmth to it, a feeling that we were all together in a very important place. A young girl sat down next to me and handed me a canteen of cool water. "Here," she said, "have a drink." I drank it down and passed it to Skip who passed it to someone else. That was the feeling that day. We all seemed to be sharing everything.

We listened as the speakers one after another denounced the invasion of Cambodia and the slaying of the students at Kent State. The sun was getting very hot and Skip and I decided to move around. We wanted to get to the White House where Nixon was holed up, probably watching television. We were in a great sea of people, thousands and thousands all around us. We finally made it to Lafayette Park. On the other side of the avenue the government had lined up thirty or forty buses, making a huge wall between the people and the White House. I remember wondering back then why they had to put all those buses in front of the president. Was the government so afraid of its own people that it needed such a gigantic barricade? I'll always remember those buses lined up that day and not being able to see the White House from my wheelchair.

We went back to the rally for a while, then went on down to the Reflecting Pool. Hundreds of people had taken off their clothes. They were jumping up and down to the beat of bongo drums and metal cans. A man in his fifties had stripped completely naked. Wearing only a crazy-looking hat and a pair of enormous black glasses, he was dancing on a platform in the middle of hundreds of naked people. The crowd was clapping wildly. Skip hesitated for a moment, then stripped all his clothes off, jumping into the pool and joining the rest of the people. I didn't know what all of this had to do with the invasion of Cambodia or the students slain at Kent State, but it was total freedom. As I sat there in my wheelchair at the edge of the Reflecting Pool with everyone running naked all around me and the clapping and the drums resounding in my ears, I wanted to join them. I wanted to take off my clothes like Skip and the rest of them and wade into the pool and rub my body with all those others. Everything seemed to be hitting me all at once. One part of me was upset that people were swimming naked in the national monument and the other part of me completely understood that now it was their pool, and what good is a pool if you can't swim in it.

I remember how the police came later that day, very suddenly, when we were watching the sun go down—a blue legion of police in cars and on motorcycles and others with angry faces on big horses. A tall cop walked into the crowd near the Reflecting Pool and read something into a bullhorn no one could make out. The drums stopped and a few of the naked people began to put their clothes back on. It was almost evening and with most of the invading army's forces heading back along the Jersey Turnpike, the blue legion had decided to attack. And they did— wading their horses into the pool, flailing their clubs, smashing skulls. People were running everywhere as gas canisters began to pop. I couldn't understand why this was happening, why the police would attack the people, running them into the grass with their horses and beating them with their clubs. Two or three horses charged into the crowd at full gallop, driving the invading army into retreat toward the Lincoln Memorial. A girl was crying and screaming, trying to help her bleeding friend. She was yelling something about the pigs and kept stepping backward away from the horses and the flying clubs. For the first time that day I felt anger surge up inside me. I was no longer an observer, sitting in my car at the edge of a demonstration. I was right in the middle of it and it was ugly. Skip started pushing the chair as fast as he could up the path toward the Lincoln Memorial. I kept turning, looking back. I wanted to shout back at the charging police, tell them I was a veteran.

When we got to the memorial, I remember looking at Lincoln's face and reading the words carved on the walls in back of him. I felt certain that if he were alive he would be there with us.

I told Skip that I was never going to be the same. The demonstration had stirred something in my mind that would be there from now on. It was so very different from boot camp and fighting in the war. There was a togetherness, just as there had been in Vietnam, but it was a togetherness of a different kind of people and for a much different reason. In the war we were killing and maiming people. In Washington on that Saturday afternoon in May we were trying to heal them and set them free. ❧

Ron Kovic

RESPONDING TO CLUSTER THREE

WHAT WAS HAPPENING BACK HOME?

Thinking Skill GENERALIZING

1. There was an immediate and overwhelming reaction of disbelief and outrage after Nixon's Cambodia speech. Why do you think this was so? Explain your answer.

2. What do you think Woodstock represented to America's youth and to the establishment? **Compare and contrast** the reactions.

3. The phrase "generation gap" was coined during the 1960s to describe the growing distrust and misunderstanding between the youthful counterculture and older generation or establishment. Use a chart such as the one below to gather details about both sides of the generation gap. Then use the details to write a **general statement** about each side. Be sure to base your generalizations on specific details.

Selection	Characteristics of Establishment	Characteristics of Counterculture
Law and Order Chicago Style	brutal; rude; believed in the war; believed in law and order; threatened bystanders	chanted obscenities; waved Viet Cong flags; littered; wore long hair; went barefoot; camped in the park
Like a Rolling Stone		
Woodstock Nation and Woodstock:The Oral History		
A State of Emergency at the People's Republic of Berkeley		
Born on the Fourth of July		
Generalization		

4. Why do you think the authorities in Chicago, Berkeley, and Kent State reacted so strongly to the protesters?

Writing Activity: Dueling Letters to the Editor

Readers of newspapers often vent their emotions by writing letters to the editor. With a partner, chose one of the incidents in this cluster. Each of you should write a letter to the editor about the incident, with one taking the side of the counterculture and the other taking the side of the establishment.

A Strong Letter to the Editor

- states your position.
- backs it up with details and/or facts.
- sometimes uses personal experience or emotion to persuade readers.
- ends with a call to action telling what you want readers to believe or do.

CLUSTER FOUR

Thinking on Your Own
Thinking Skill SYNTHESIZING

Where Have All the Flowers Gone?

PETE SEEGER

Where have all the flowers gone, long time passing?
Where have all the flowers gone, long time ago?
Where have all the flowers gone?
Gone to young girls, every one!
When will they ever learn, when will they ever learn?

Where have all the young girls gone, long time passing?
Where have all the young girls gone, long time ago?
Where have all the young girls gone?
Gone to young men, every one!
When will they ever learn, when will they ever learn?

Where have all the young men gone, long time passing?
Where have all the young men gone, long time ago?
Where have all the young men gone?
Gone to soldiers, every one!
When will they ever learn, when will they ever learn?

Where have all the soldiers gone, long time passing?
Where have all the soldiers gone, long time ago?
Where have all the soldiers gone?
Gone to graveyards, every one!
When will they ever learn, when will they ever learn?

Where have all the graveyards gone, long time passing?
Where have all the graveyards gone, long time ago?
Where have all the graveyards gone?
Gone to flowers, every one!
When will they ever learn, oh when will they ever learn?

Epilogue

PHILIP CAPUTO

We were crouched in the second-floor corridor of the Continental Palace Hotel, wondering if the North Vietnamese Army had finally invaded Saigon, hoping it had not. The century-old walls trembled slightly from the concussion of the seven-hundred-pound bombs enemy planes were dropping on Tan Son Nhut airbase, five miles away. Every policeman and soldier in the city seemed to be firing a rifle or machine gun. The noise was deafening. Cringing in the hallway, we had no way of knowing whether the shooting was still directed at the planes or if a full-scale, street-to-street battle for the capital had begun. Having spent the past month observing the South Vietnamese Army losing one battle after another, there was no doubt in our minds that they would lose this one too. There was considerable doubt about our own future. As we listened to the thud of bombs and the rattle of small-arms fire, we asked each other unanswerable questions. Would there be enough time for an evacuation? If not, how would we, American correspondents, be treated by the Communist victors? In the final moments of chaos, would the South Vietnamese, feeling betrayed by Washington, turn their weapons on every American they saw?

It was useless to speculate under the circumstances. One of our more practical members suggested that we forgo debating what might happen and find out what was happening. After some hesitation, we left the shelter of the corridor and walked downstairs to the lobby. It was filled with frightened civilians and weeping children who had been driven in off the streets by gunfire. The hotel's high, wooden door was now barred, like the gate to a medieval castle. Four of us opened it cautiously and went outside.

The small-arms fire was still heavy, but it seemed aimed at the enemy jets that whined over the city, heading with their bombs for the airbase. We saw no green-clad soldiers in pith helmets—the enemy's distinctive headgear. There were quite a few policemen, ARVN[1] soldiers, and other newsmen running down the streets. They were as confused as we. Together with my colleague from the Chicago *Tribune*, Ron Yates, I jogged over to the UPI offices, a block from the hotel.

We found confusion there as well. One reporter was melodramatically typing out a story while dressed in a helmet and flak jacket. Teletype machines clacked urgently. After reading the wire services' dispatches, Yates and I decided that the final crisis, though near, had not yet arrived. Enemy units were still a day's fighting from the city. Assuming that the American embassy would order an evacuation the following day, Yates and I went back to the hotel to pack our gear. It was dark by the time we finished. The air raid was over. Through the window of my top-floor room, I could see the flames of a burning fuel dump. Gekko lizards clung to the room's white walls, the walls quaking from the secondary explosions set off by the bombs, the lizards immobile in their reptilian indifference.

I dragged my gear down to Nick Proffitt's room, which was two floors below. Proffitt, the correspondent for *Newsweek*, had taken me in the week before when an enemy rocket had devastated the top floors of the nearby Metropole Hotel. Having survived one month of the 1975 offensive in Vietnam, I had no intention of being blown to bits in bed. Proffitt had kidded me about my fears. I didn't mind. He could kid me all he wanted. At thirty-three, with a wife and two children to support, I no longer felt the need to prove anything to anyone.

Proffitt and I fell asleep in the early-morning hours. Lying on the floor behind the furniture with which I had barricaded the window, I was jarred awake when the North Vietnamese began shelling Tan Son Nhut and part of the city with rockets and 130-mm field guns. It was April 29. The bombardment went on for six hours. Around ten-thirty, a reporter who had a citizens' band radio tuned to the American embassy's frequency announced, "They've just passed the word. That's it. It's one-hundred-percent evacuation. It's bye-bye everybody."

A hasty, undignified exit followed. Crowds of newsmen, embassy officials, Vietnamese civilians, and various other "evacuees" stumbled down

---

1 **ARVN:** Army of the Republic of Vietnam (South Vietnam)

the half-deserted streets toward the evacuation points. I passed a group of ARVN militiamen and smiled at them wanly. "You go home now?" one of them asked. "Americans di-di?"[2]

"Yes," I said, feeling like a deserter, "Americans di-di."

Our motley column was eventually directed to a staging area across the street from a hospital. Columns of smoke were rising from the city's outskirts, and someone said that North Vietnamese troops had been spotted only two miles from where we were standing. We stood about, dripping sweat and listening to the steady thud of the incoming one-thirties.[3] Finally, two olive-drab buses, led by a car with a flashing mars light, pulled up. We piled on board, some sixty or seventy crammed on each bus, the small convoy heading for Tan Son Nhut.

We were just passing through the airport's main gate as a South Vietnamese plane took off from the smoking, cratered runway. An old C-119 cargo plane, it had not climbed more than a few hundred feet when a spiraling fireball rose up behind it. There was a great boom as the anti-aircraft missile slammed into the C-119 and sent it crashing into the city. Our nervousness turned to fear, for we were to be evacuated by helicopter. Easy targets.

The buses stopped in front of a complex of buildings known as the Defense Attaché's Office. During the height of American involvement in the war, the complex had been called Pentagon East. It had served as Westmoreland's headquarters. The tennis courts nearby were to be the landing zone for the helicopters. We clambered off the buses, spurred on by a heavy shell that banged into the tarmac seventy-five yards away. "Don't panic," someone said in a voice several octaves higher than normal.

Inside the building, we were lined up, divided into helicopter teams, and tagged. Every foot of every long corridor in the building was filled with Americans, Vietnamese refugees, newsmen from a dozen different countries, even a few old French plantation owners. The walls shook from the blasts of the shells hitting the runway. Small-arms fire crackled at the perimeter of the airbase. It was going to be a hot LZ.[4] I hoped it would be my last one, and I tried not to think about those anti-aircraft missiles.

We sweated it out in there until the late afternoon, when the first of the Marine helicopters arrived. They were big CH-53s, each capable of

2 **di-di:** Vietnamese slang for "go"

3 **one-thirties:** shells from 130-mm canons

4 **LZ:** landing zone

Evacuation from the roof of the U.S. Embassy in Saigon.

holding as many people as a small airliner. "Okay, let's go!" yelled a Marine sergeant from the embassy guard. "Let's go. Drop all your luggage. No room for that. Move! Move! Move!" I dropped the valise I had lugged around all day and dashed out the door, running across the tennis courts toward the aircraft. Marine riflemen were crouched around the LZ, their weapons pointed toward the trees and rice paddies at the fringes of the airfield. Together with some sixty other people, half of them Vietnamese civilians and ARVN officers, I scrambled on board one of the CH-53s.

The helicopter lifted off, climbing rapidly. Within minutes, we were at six thousand feet, the wreckage of the South Vietnamese cargo plane burning far below. It was all so familiar: the deafening racket inside the helicopter; the door gunners crouched behind their machine guns, muzzles pointed down at the green and brown gridwork of the Mekong Delta through which flooded rivers spread like a network of blood vessels; and the expectant waiting—terrifying and yet exhilarating—as we looked for tracers or for the bright corkscrewing ball of a heat-seeking missile. One started to come up, but the lead helicopter in our flight diverted it with a decoy flare that simulated an aircraft engine's heat. We took some ground fire—fire from South Vietnamese soldiers who probably felt that the Americans had betrayed them.

My mind shot back a decade, to that day we had marched into Vietnam, swaggering, confident, and full of idealism. We had believed we were there for a high moral purpose. But somehow our idealism was lost, our morals corrupted, and the purpose forgotten.

We reached the coast about twenty minutes later. We were out of danger, out of range of the missiles, removed from all possibility of being among the last Americans to die in Vietnam. Relaxing their grip on the .50-caliber machine guns, the door gunners grinned and flashed the thumbs-up sign. Swooping out over the South China Sea, over the thousands of fishing junks jammed with refugees, the CH-53 touched down on the U.S.S. *Denver*, a helicopter assault ship that was part of the armada the Seventh Fleet had assembled for the evacuation. There was some applause as the aircraft settled down on the flight deck and as we filed out, a marine slapped me on the back and said, "Welcome home. Bet you're glad to be out of there." I was, of course. I asked him which outfit he was from. "Ninth MEB," he answered. The 9th Expeditionary Brigade, the same unit with which I had landed at Danang. But the men who belonged to it now seemed a good deal more cynical than we who had belonged to it ten years before. The marine looked at the faint blue line marking the Vietnamese coast and said, "Well, that's one country we don't have to give billions of dollars to anymore."

The evacuees were processed and sent down to the scorching mess deck for a meal. Most of us were giddy with relief, but one disconsolate diplomat from the American embassy just sat and muttered to himself, "It's over. It's the end. It's the end of an era. It was a lousy way to have it end, but I guess it had to end some way." Exhausted and sweating, he just shook his head. "The end of an era." I supposed it was, but I was much too tired to reflect on the historical significance of the event in which I had just taken part: America had lost its first war.

The next day, April 30, the ship's captain announced that the Saigon government had surrendered to the North Vietnamese. We took the news quietly. It was over. ❧

A President's Pain

President Gerald R. Ford

Washington, D.C., April 29, 1975
As Americans and South Vietnamese fled by helicopter from the U.S.
Embassy in Saigon, President Gerald R. Ford watched in anguish.

That was probably the hardest day of my presidency for me. I had supported Kennedy when he sent our first combat troops to Vietnam. I supported Johnson even though I differed on some of his military strategy, but I supported the effort to try to win the war. I did the same with Nixon, and with all my support, I'm the president who ends up losing the war.

You have no idea how painful it was. To sit in the Oval Office and watch on TV the American troops, military, civilians being evacuated along with as many South Vietnamese as we could who had supported us. And we had a conflict. The Secretary of Defense, Jim Schlesinger, had wanted us to get out of Saigon a week earlier. And then we had Graham Martin, the ambassador. He wanted to stay until the North Vietnamese shot him. So we were torn, Henry Kissinger and myself, between the two extremes. And I made the decision, and Henry fully agreed, that we would stay as long as possible to get all our military, many of our civilians, and as many as we could of our South Vietnamese allies out. I think we made a very heroic effort and did the best we could under the worst of circumstances. I look upon it as the sadness of a retreat that I'll never forget. ∾

The Summer of Vietnam

BARBARA RENAUD GONZÁLEZ

So, what are you writing about? I ask Bill Broyles, the former *Newsweek Magazine* goldenboy. He's the Texas man who can write *anything* and get it published. Unlike me.

"Vietnam," he says. The worst answer. The only answer that can make me cry.

Instead, at night I remember.

Ernesto Sanchez is Vietnam to me. Born July 9, 1947. In a place called Kennedy, Texas. Died in the summer of 1967, somewhere in Vietnam. Somewhere in my 13th summer.

This is my Vietnam.

I sang love songs to them. Made up Ken dolls after them. Imagined kissing them. I still do. Marine-boys. Boys in dress green with stiff brass buttons that would catch your breaking heart when they gave you the biggest *abrazo*[1] of your life. Then they always died in Vietnam.

Always teasing me. "This last dance is for you Barbara," they'd say. Taught me to dance those skip-steps of adolescence. Told me they'd wait

---

1 *abrazo*: Spanish for "hug" or "embrace"

for me. And they never came back from Vietnam to see how I'd grown up for them.

I knew they would not die. Heroes don't die in the movies, after all. The good guys always win. Who would dare extinguish the crooked smile football hands and Aqua Velva faces I knew so well? My brothers-at-war.

Of the 3,427 Texas men who died in Vietnam, 22 percent were Latinos. And another 17 percent of the dead were African-American. The minorities were not a minority in the platoons, but a majority of the frightened faces. And one-third of the body bags.

This at a time when Latinos constituted 12 percent of the population.

But the machismo goes a long way in war. We Latinos received more medals, thirteen of the prestigious Medal of Honor, than any other group.

We can count soldiers in the American Revolution (as Spaniards), the Roosevelt Rough Riders,[2] both sides of the Civil War, and plenty of fathers and abuelitos[3] in the world wars. Soldiering doesn't require U.S. citizenship, and no one cares if you crossed the border if you're willing to fight on our side.

We lost our best men in Vietnam. Isaac Camacho died first in 1963, Everett Alvares was the first American pilot shot down, spending eight-and-a-half years as a POW. Juan Valdez was in the last helicopter leaving Vietnam. First in, last out. They didn't go to Canada or Mexico. They went directly to Vietnam.

But from Oliver Stone,[4] you would think that all our boys looked like Tom Cruise. Or agonized at China Beach.[5] No. They were my brothers, uncles, cousins, my heroes.

Sometimes it looks as if they died for nothing. Impossible. It cannot be. Blood lost is blood redeemed, they say. What is the boy worth? If he died for all of us, then we must gain in proportion to the sacrifice. A Medal of Honor for the neighborhood school. Some Distinguished Service Crosses for family housing. Maybe the Bronze Stars for the judge or councilman. Flying Crosses for a good job. And a Purple Heart for a mother who still cries in Spanish. ❧

---

2 **Roosevelt Rough Riders:** a calvary unit led by Theodore Roosevelt during the Spanish-American War

3 **abuelitos:** Spanish for "grandfathers"

4 **Oliver Stone:** a director of three films about Vietnam, including one starring Tom Cruise

5 **China Beach:** a U.S. relaxation camp on the China Sea near Non Nuoc, Vietnam; also the title of a 1980s television drama about nurses in Vietnam

Stop the Sun

GARY PAULSEN

Terry Erickson was a tall boy, 13, starting to fill out with muscle but still as little awkward. He was on the edge of being a good athlete, which meant a lot to him. He felt it coming too slowly, though, and that bothered him.

But what bothered him even more was when his father's eyes went away.

Usually it happened when it didn't cause any particular trouble. Sometimes during a meal his father's fork would stop halfway to his mouth, just stop, and there would be a long pause while the eyes went away, far away.

After several minutes his mother would reach over and take the fork and put it gently down on his plate, and they would go back to eating—or try to go back to eating—normally.

They knew what caused it. When it first started, Terry had asked his mother in private what it was, what was causing the strange behavior.

"It's from the war," his mother had said. "The doctors at the veterans' hospital call it the Vietnam syndrome."

"Will it go away?"

"They don't know. Sometimes it goes away. Sometimes it doesn't. They are trying to help him."

"But what happened? What actually caused it?"

"I told you. Vietnam."

"But there had to be something," Terry persisted. "Something made him like that. Not just Vietnam. Billy's father was there, and he doesn't act that way."

"That's enough questions," his mother said sternly. "He doesn't talk about it, and I don't ask. Neither will you. Do you understand?"

"But, Mom."

"That's enough."

And he stopped pushing it. But it bothered him whenever it happened. When something bothered him, he liked to stay with it until he understood it, and he understood no part of this.

Words. His father had trouble, and they gave him words like Vietnam syndrome. He knew almost nothing of the war, and when he tried to find out about it he kept hitting walls. Once he went to the school library and asked for anything they might have that could help him understand the war and how it affected his father. They gave him a dry history that described French involvement, Communist involvement, American involvement. But it told him nothing of the war. It was all numbers, cold numbers, and nothing of what had *happened*. There just didn't seem to be anything that could help him.

Another time he stayed after class and tried to talk to Mr. Carlson, who taught history. But some part of Terry was embarrassed. He didn't want to say why he wanted to know about Vietnam, so he couldn't be specific.

"What do you want to know about Vietnam, Terry?" Mr. Carlson had asked. "It was a big war."

Terry had looked at him, and something had started up in his mind, but he didn't let it out. He shrugged. "I just want to know what it was like. I know somebody who was in it."

"A friend?"

"Yessir. A good friend."

Mr. Carlson had studied him, looking into his eyes, but didn't ask any other questions. Instead he mentioned a couple of books Terry had not seen. They turned out to be pretty good. They told about how it felt to be in combat. Still, he couldn't make his father be one of the men he read about.

And it may have gone on and on like that, with Terry never really knowing any more about it, except that his father's eyes started going away more and more often. It might have just gone the rest of his life that way except for the shopping mall.

It was easily the most embarrassing thing that had ever happened to him.

It started as a normal shopping trip. His father had to go to the hardware store, and he asked Terry to go along.

When they got to the mall, they split up. His father went to the hardware store, Terry to a record store to look at albums.

Terry browsed so long that he was late meeting his father at the mall's front door. But his father wasn't there, and Terry looked out to the car to make sure it was still in the parking lot. It was, and he supposed his father had gotten busy, so he waited.

Still his father didn't come, and he was about to go to the hardware store to find him when he noticed the commotion. Or not a commotion so much as a sudden movement of people.

Later, he thought of it and couldn't remember when the feeling first came to him that there was something wrong. The people were moving toward the hardware store, and that might have been what made Terry suspicious.

There was a crowd blocking the entry to the story, and he couldn't see what they were looking at. Some of them where laughing small, nervous laughs that made no sense.

Terry squeezed through the crowd until he got near the front. At first he saw nothing unusual. There were still some people in front of him, so he pushed a crack between them. Then he saw it: His father was squirming along on the floor on his stomach. He was crying, looking terrified, his breath coming in short, hot pants like some kind of hurt animal.

It burned into Terry's mind, the picture of his father down on the floor. It burned in and in, and he wanted to walk away, but something made him move forward. He knelt next to his father and helped the owner of the store get him up on his feet. His father didn't speak at all but continued to make little whimpering sounds, and they lead him back into the owner's office and put him in a chair. Then Terry called his mother, and she came in a taxi to take them home. Waiting, Terry sat in a chair next to his father, looking at the floor, wanting only for the earth to open and let him drop in a deep hole. He wanted to disappear.

Words. They gave him words like Vietnam syndrome, and his father was crawling through a hardware store on his stomach.

When the embarrassment became so bad that he would cross the street when he saw his father coming, when it ate into him as he went to sleep, Terry realized he had to do something. He had to know this thing, had to understand what was wrong with his father.

When it came, it was simple enough at the start. It had taken some courage, more than Terry thought he could find. His father was sitting in the kitchen at the table, and his mother had gone shopping. Terry wanted it that way; he wanted his father alone. His mother seemed to try to protect him, as if his father could break.

Terry got a soda out of the refrigerator and popped it open. As an afterthought, he handed it to his father and got out another for himself. Then he sat at the table.

His father smiled. "You look serious."

"Well . . ."

It went nowhere for a moment, and Terry was just about to drop it altogether. It may be the wrong time, he thought, but there might never be a better one. He tightened his back, took a sip of pop.

"I was wondering if we could talk about something, Dad," Terry said.

His father shrugged. "We already did the bit about girls. Some time ago, as I remember it."

"No, not that." It was a standing joke between them. When his father finally got around to explaining things to him, they'd already covered it in school. "It's something else."

"Something pretty heavy, judging by your face."

"Yes."

"Well?"

I still can't do it, Terry thought. Things are bad, but maybe not as bad as they could get. I can still drop this thing.

"Vietnam," Terry blurted out. And he thought, there, it's out, it's out and gone.

"No!" his father said sharply. It was as if he had been struck a blow. A body blow.

"But, Dad."

"No. That's another part of my life. A bad part. A rotten part. It was before I met your mother, long before you. It has nothing to do with this family, nothing. No."

So, Terry thought, so I tried. But it wasn't over yet. It wasn't started yet.

"It just seems to bother you so much," Terry said, "and I thought if I could help or maybe understand it better . . ." His words ran until he foundered, until he could say no more. He looked at the table, then out the window. It was all wrong to bring it up, he thought. I blew it all up. "I'm sorry."

But now his father didn't hear him. Now his father's eyes were gone again, and a shaft of something horrible went through Terry's heart as he thought he had done this thing to his father, caused his eyes to go away.

"You can't know," his father said after a time. "You can't know this thing."

Terry said nothing. He felt he had said too much.

"This thing that you want to know—there is so much of it that you cannot know it all, and to know only a part is . . . is too awful. I can't tell you. I can't tell anybody what it was really like."

It was more than he'd ever said about Vietnam, and his voice was breaking. Terry hated himself and felt he would hate himself until he was an old man. In one second he had caused so much ruin. And all because he had been embarrassed. What difference did it make? Now he had done this, and he wanted to hide, to leave. But he sat, waiting, knowing that it wasn't done.

His father looked to him, through him, somewhere into and out of Terry. He wasn't in the kitchen anymore. He wasn't in the house. He was back in the green places, back in the hot places, the wet-hot places.

"You think that because I act strange, we can talk and it will be all right," his father said. "That we can talk and it will just go away. That's what you think, isn't it?"

Terry started to shake his head, but he knew it wasn't expected.

"That's what the shrinks say," his father continued. "The psychiatrists tell me that if I talk about it, the whole thing will go away. But they don't know. They weren't there. You weren't there. Nobody was there but me and some other dead people, and they can't talk because they couldn't stop the morning."

Terry pushed his soda can back and forth, looking down, frightened at what was happening. *The other dead people,* he'd said, as if he were dead as well. *Couldn't stop the morning.*

"I don't understand, Dad."

"No. You don't." His voice hardened, then softened again and broke at the edges. "But see, see how it was . . ."

He trailed off, and Terry thought he was done. His father looked back down at the table, at the can of soda he hadn't touched, at the tablecloth, at his hands, which were folded, inert on the table.

"We were crossing a rice paddy in the dark," he said, and suddenly his voice flowed like a river breaking loose. "We were crossing the paddy, and it was dark, still dark, so black you couldn't see the end of your nose. There was a light rain, a mist, and I was thinking that during the next break I would whisper and tell Petey Kressler how nice the rain felt, but of course I didn't know there wouldn't be a Petey Kressler."

He took a deep, ragged breath. At that moment Terry felt his brain swirl, a kind of whirlpool pulling, and he felt the darkness and the light rain because it was in his father's eyes, in his voice.

"So we were crossing the paddy, and it was a straight sweep, and then we caught it. We began taking fire from three sides, automatic weapons, and everybody went down and tried to get low, but we couldn't. We couldn't get low enough. We could never get low enough, and you could hear the rounds hitting people. It was just a short time before they brought in the mortars, and we should have moved, should have run, but nobody got up, and after a time, nobody *could* get up. The fire just kept coming and coming, and then incoming mortars, and I heard screams as they hit, but there was nothing to do. Nothing to do."

"Dad?" Terry said. He thought, maybe I can stop him. Maybe I can stop him before . . . before it gets to be too much. Before he breaks.

"Mortars," his father went on, "I hated mortars. You just heard them *wump* as they fired, and you didn't know where they would hit, and you always felt like they would hit your back. They swept back and forth with the mortars, and the automatic weapons kept coming in, and there was no radio, no way to call for artillery. Just the dark to hide in. So I crawled to the side and found Jackson, only he wasn't there, just part of his body, the top part, and I hid under it and waited, and waited, and waited.

"Finally the firing quit. But see, see how it was in the dark with nobody alive but me? I yelled once, but that brought fire again, so I shut up, and there was nothing, not even the screams."

His father cried, and Terry tried to understand, and he thought he could feel part of it. But it was so much, so much and so strange to him.

"You cannot know this," his father repeated. It was almost a chant. "You cannot know the fear. It was dark, and I was the only one left alive out of fifty-four men, all dead but me, and I knew that the Vietcong were just waiting for the light. When the dawn came, 'Charley' would come and finish everybody off, the way they always did. And I thought if I could stop the dawn, just stop the sun from coming up, I could make it."

Terry felt the fear, and he also felt the tears coming down his cheeks. His hand went out across the table, and he took his father's hand and held it. It was shaking.

"I mean I actually thought that if I could stop the sun from coming up, I could live. I made my brain work on that because it was all I had. Through the rest of the night in the rain in the paddy, I thought I could do it. I could stop the dawn." He took a deep breath. "But you can't, you know. You can't stop it from coming, and when I saw the gray light, I knew I was dead. It would just be minutes, and the light would be full, and I just settled under Jackson's body and hid."

He stopped, and his face came down into his hands. Terry stood and went around the table to stand in back of him, his hands on his shoulders, rubbing gently.

"They didn't shoot me. They came, one of them poked Jackson's body and went on and they left me. But I was dead. I'm still dead, don't you see? I died because I couldn't stop the sun. I died. Inside where I am— I died."

Terry was still in back of him, and he nodded, but he didn't see. Not that. He understood only that he didn't understand and that he would probably never know what it was really like, would probably never understand what had truly happened. And maybe his father would never be truly normal.

But Terry also knew that it didn't matter. He would try to understand, and the trying would have to be enough. He would try hard from now on, and he would not be embarrassed when his father's eyes went away. He would not be embarrassed no matter what his father did. Terry had knowledge now. Maybe not enough and maybe not all that he would need.

But it was a start. ౦౪

To Heal a Nation

Joel L. Swerdlow

For these GIs, coming home had not been like John Wayne had promised. They had gone to Vietnam filled with images of John F. Kennedy and Hollywood movies, and they did their duty, even though few of these images matched the muck and the moral confusion they found in Indochina. After 12 months they were put on an air-conditioned airplane with pretty stewardesses, and suddenly the war was over. "Wash up," one returning veteran's mother had said. "Your welcome-home dinner is ready." He looked down at his hands. Mud from Vietnam was still under his fingernails.

No one wanted to hear what the vets had been through. People who saw them in uniform might spit, shout "Murderer," or ask, "How come you were stupid enough to go?" Or, if you'd arrived home blind or missing an arm or a leg, someone might come up and say, "Served you right."

Thus, many vets carried powerful and disturbing feelings that were buried deeper and deeper as the war became old news to other Americans.

For Jan Scruggs—wounded and decorated for bravery when only 19 years old in 1969—the feelings surfaced in March 1979 after he saw *The Deer Hunter,* an emotional movie about combat in Vietnam. "I'm going to build a memorial to all the guys who served in Vietnam," Scruggs told his wife. "It'll have the names of everyone killed."

Scruggs soon afterward presented his dream to a meeting of Vietnam vets. "We'll accept no money from the government," the son of a milk-man from rural Maryland said. "Dollars will come in from the American people." You're naïve, they told him. The country will never go for it.

At a press conference Scruggs explained that the Vietnam veteran could be honored without taking a position on the war, that the warrior could be separated from the war. He was enthusiastic and not embarrassed to let his feelings show. "The only thing we're worried about," he concluded, "is raising too much money."

Money did start coming in. Five dollars from an unemployed vet. Ten dollars from a young girl in memory of her father. One check came with only a torn piece of paper carrying the name of a dead GI. "All we want is for people to recognize the sacrifices and contributions they made because the country they love told them it was right," one man wrote.

On the CBS Evening News, Roger Mudd reported that the veterans organization whose only concern had been about raising too much money had gathered the grand sum of $144.50.

Later, a comedian on a network program made fun of Scruggs. It was a good joke, and audience laughed.

Two other Vietnam vets were not laughing. Robert Doubek and John Wheeler, both attorneys in Washington, D.C., had begun working with Scruggs. Calls went out, and Bob Doubek and Jack Wheeler had no difficulty recruiting a group, organized into the nonprofit Vietnam Veterans Memorial Fund, willing to volunteer thousands of hours at no pay.

A *Washington Post* article by Scruggs placed the VVMF's[1] motives clearly on the public record: "If the war was unpopular at home, it was probably liked even less by those whose fate it was to serve in Vietnam. It was a year-long nightmare. Half the men in my company were killed or wounded. . . . A few months before leaving Vietnam I spent four hours of my life 50 feet from a North Vietnamese machine-gun emplacement. A dozen American youths were pinned down; several were wounded. . . . One fellow exposed himself to the enemy gunners and drew their fire. . . . Then came his screams. . . . We knew we were watching the man who had given his life for us die. . . .

"The bitterness I feel when I remember carrying the lifeless bodies of close friends through the mire of Vietnam will probably never subside. I still wonder if anything can be found to bring any purpose to all the suffering and death."

In September, Doubek, Wheeler, and Scruggs met with Senator Charles McC. Mathias, Jr. (R-Md.), whom Scruggs had recruited to their

---

1 **VVMF's:** Vietnam Veterans Memorial Fund's

cause, and a National Park Service official, who spread out a map of the Washington metropolitan area.

Mathias put his thumb on the map. "How about this?" he said.

Wheeler and Doubek looked down. Mathias's thumb was on the Mall, right next to the Lincoln Memorial.

The vets formed a National Sponsoring Committee—which included First Lady Rosalynn Carter, former President Gerald Ford, Gen. William Westmoreland, and Senator George McGovern—and mailed out a fund-raising appeal signed by Bob Hope. Tens of thousands of dollars came back, but response to the Hope letter mostly showed how much the memorial was needed:

"My son was killed, and I can't bring it up during a party."

"I did not expect a ticker tape parade, but I served my country faithfully."

"I hope the monument will be built in my lifetime."

"For my son, so he can ask the questions I'll never be able to answer."

"Look at the sheer whimsy of it all. They are dead. I am not."

"Anyone who died in that fiasco is a hero in my eyes."

"Our son did not come home to us."

"Those boys, God bless, were given a *rotten* deal."

Not everyone loved the idea. "To me you are a bunch of crying babies," a man wrote. At the meeting of one government agency, a military officer had even asked, in effect, "Why build a memorial to losers?"

The chief source of potential opposition seemed to be the antiwar movement. "Let's not perpetuate the memory of such dishonorable events by erecting monuments to them," one person wrote. A reporter telephoned Scruggs, and from his questions made clear his antiwar views. "You're real egomaniacs," the reporter finally said. "You're building a memorial to yourselves."

Sensitive to the emotional minefield they were entering, Jack Wheeler warned his colleagues to take no political position and to express no opinions on Vietnam-related subjects. The stakes were far greater than simply building a memorial. "We have become," he said, "trustees of a portion of the national heart."

The site next to Lincoln was perfect. To leave site selection in the hands of an official such as the Secretary of the Interior, however, could mean an out-of-the-way location. The only way to get their land near Lincoln was to get Congress to give it directly to them. If the Vietnam Veterans Memorial was to help bind the nation's wounds, what better place could there be?

Hearings before a Senate subcommittee were scheduled for March 12, 1980. Jan Scruggs with a suitcase full of documents justifying the site on the Mall was in his car, and he couldn't find a parking place. He pulled into a parking lot reserved for senators.

"Listen," Scruggs told the guard, "I've got to testify for the Vietnam memorial. Hearings start in seven minutes."

"Third Marines. Two tours," the guard said, motioning Scruggs into a senator's parking slot.

Congress was doing little for Vietnam vets, yet many senators supported the VVMF because it was asking for land and not tax dollars. The VVMF, with little public attention, soon had 95 Senate cosponsors. Scruggs called the remaining five. "We have 99 cosponsors," he told each. "The Associated Press wants to know who the holdout is." Within hours 100 Senators, the entire U.S. Senate, had signed up.

The bill, giving the vets two acres at the foot of Abraham Lincoln, passed the Senate in just seven minutes on April 30, 1980, but procedural difficulties in the House of Representatives delayed final action until after Memorial Day.

The VVMF, however, still held services at the site. About 400 people attended. Couples held hands or hugged children, and former GIs wearing jungle fatigues or ribbons pinned on business suits stood in tight clusters, as though sheer body proximity helped them share their emotions. Jack Wheeler stepped to the microphone. "There's no more sacred part of a person than his or her name," he said. "We have to start remembering real, individual names."

Members of the audience came up, one by one, to say the name of someone they had lost. My son. My husband. My father. My fiancé. My buddy. My brother. My childhood friend. My classmate. We still love them. We remember.

▲   ▲   ▲

On July 1, 1980, President Jimmy Carter signed the bill into law. The vets had their land. George Washington, Thomas Jefferson, and Abraham Lincoln would have new neighbors: every GI who served in America's most hated war.

The vets spent considerable time arguing about how best to get their design. Jan Scruggs found the whole issue boring. "Let's put the names on the Mall and call it a day," he said. Finally the VVMF decided to recruit a world-class jury that would, in turn, prompt the nation's best designers to submit entries. Any U.S. citizen 18 or older would be eligible to compete. Bob Doubek wrote out the basic philosophy behind the competition: "Because of inequities in the draft system, the brunt of dangerous service fell upon the young, often the socially and economically disadvantaged. [However] the memorial will make no political statement regarding the war or its conduct. It will transcend those issues. The hope is that the creation of the memorial will begin a healing process."

When the March 31, 1981, deadline arrived, the VVMF had received 1,421 entries. One came from a Yale student who had been given a classroom assignment to design a Vietnam veterans memorial. In late November she and three classmates had driven to Washington to examine the site. It was a cold, clear day, and the only other people nearby were a few Frisbee players. After several minutes she decided that the earth should be cut open, with stone exposed in the wound as part of the healing process. She also thought about death. To her, it was an abstract concept. She was 20 years old, and no one close to her had ever died.

Back at school it took less than three weeks to complete her design, which she saw as "visual poetry."

To help draw attention to the memorial, a former infantryman and a former paratrooper walked 818 miles from Jacksonville, Illinois, to Washington. At the Ohio-Indiana border they were joined by a man who said, "My wife and I want to see our son's name on the monument."

On April 26, about 150 people, including vets on crutches and in wheelchairs, joined the walkers as they crossed the Potomac River. "It would have been nice to have a bigger reception for those guys," Scruggs told reporters waiting at the memorial site. "Well, maybe the Americans killed in Vietnam don't mean that much to a lot of people."

The next day the design jury began four days of closed-door deliberations. The proposed memorials came in all shapes, including hovering helicopters, miniature Lincoln Memorials, peace signs, and Army helmets.

After the first day a juror bumped into a friend in a hotel lobby.

"How's it going?" the friend asked.

"Very strange. One design keeps haunting me."

By noon the next day 1,189 submissions had been eliminated. The remaining 232 were placed together for further examination. That evening the juror once again saw his friend. The juror shook his head. "It's still haunting me," he said.

On the third day the jury was down to 39 entries. Number 1,026 generated the most comments: "There's no escape from its power." "A confused age needs a simple solution." "Totally eloquent." "No other place in the world like that." "Looks back to death and forward to life." "Note the reflectiveness." "Presents both solitude and a challenge." "It's easy to love it."

After 1,026 won unanimously, the jurors voted again just to make sure. 1,026. The next day Doubek looked up number 1,026. They had expected that the winner would be a prominent professional. "Maya Ying Lin." A woman. An Oriental name. Jack Wheeler recognized her address. An undergraduate residence at Yale University.

Press reaction to the design was enthusiastic. The *New York Times* said: "[It] honors these veterans with more poignancy, surely, than most more conventional monuments. . . . This design seems able to capture all of the feelings of ambiguity and anguish that the Vietnam War evoked in this nation."

The Commission of Fine Arts and other government agencies approved Maya Lin's design, and within weeks the American people started to register their opinion. Fund-raising flourished. Another Bob Hope letter—which read, "It is our duty now to show these veterans (who have yet to receive public recognition) that you and I personally care"— brought in daily sacks of mail.

A radiothon at a shopping center was quickly mobbed. Vets and their families stopped by to tell their stories. Former POWs came to plead for funds. Fathers brought in their children to give small change. People signed over Social Security and disability checks. Nonvets came in with grocery bags filled with cash they'd collected at parties. Radiothon organizers had said at 3 p.m. Friday that they'd be happy with $35,000; by 6 p.m. Sunday, they had $250,000. "What *is* going on out there?" a reporter asked Scruggs. He could only answer, "Hooray, America."

▲ ▲ ▲

Then, on October 13, a Vietnam vet appeared before the Commission of Fine Arts and called Maya Lin's design a "black gash of shame." He had hit a nerve. The design was hard to understand, and journalists propelled antimemorial accusations—most notably that it was unheroic, unpatriotic, below ground, and death-oriented—into a civil war among vets. VVMF reassurances that the memorial would be exposed to sunlight all day, and that the names as displayed in Maya Lin's design would speak eloquently of sacrifice, commitment, and patriotism, never attracted as much attention as the attacks.

On January 4, 1982, even though more than 650,000 people had contributed more than five million dollars to build Maya Lin's design, a letter from Secretary of the Interior James Watt arrived. The memorial would not get a construction permit and was on hold until further notice.

That night Scruggs went to the site, and walked over to the Lincoln Memorial. Scruggs looked up at Lincoln. Was the dream about to die? The Civil War had been America's bloodiest conflict, and yet the memorial carried no sense of violence. It was nonpolitical. Nothing favored the North or the South. Nothing said that slavery was morally wrong. Or that the Civil War was right. Like Maya Lin's design, it provided a sense of history, it was simple, and it relied on words. People would read Lincoln's Gettysburg Address and Second Inaugural Address, think about the words, stand quietly, and let the feelings flow. They could come away different than when they arrived.

The memorial would be built. Let the American people come with their children. Let the children ask tough questions. Who are these names? What did they do? Why did they die? Did you know them? What does it mean to me?

After several lengthy, emotional meetings, a compromise was reached: A flag and a representational statue would be added, and opponents would withdraw their objections. The sculptor eventually selected, 38-year-old Washingtonian Frederick Hart, had been the highest placing sculptor in the original competition. Hart's selection symbolized how the country was pulling together. The wall and statue would come from a woman too young to have experienced the war and a man who never served in the military and said he had been gassed in an antiwar demonstration.

At 11 a.m. on Monday, March 15, Secretary Watt authorized a permit. As concrete pilings were driven 35 feet into the ground, workmen in Barre, Vermont, used massive, high-speed, diamond-tipped saws to cut 3,000 cubic feet of granite into slices that were polished first by a series of bricks and then by a felt buffer covered with tin oxide, which is finer than talc.

Guided by computer-generated drawings, workers then fabricated the stone, cutting it into about 150 panels, each of them three inches thick, 40 inches wide, and varying in height from ten feet nine inches to 18 inches.

Shipped on specially air-cushioned trucks to Memphis, Tennessee, the stone was cleaned, painted with chemicals, and allowed to dry overnight. It was covered with a photo negative that was an exact stencil of the names in the order in which they would appear on the wall; then it was exposed to light, left for a short time, washed, and gritblasted. Experiment revealed that cutting letters into the stone one-fiftieth of an inch deep made them cast too heavy a shadow. Even a small error could spoil the memorial.

Architect Kent Cooper, hired by the VVMF to develop Maya Lin's design, made the final decisions: To maximize legibility, use very fine grit, do the blasting straight in front, and stand about 18 inches away so the letters will have maximum depth with uniform shadow. The letters would be .53 inches high and .015 inches deep.

Bob Doubek supervised compilation of the names. Many cases were heartbreaking. Veterans had been slowly dying from war-related causes for years. Some of them were in comas. Some had died in training or while on their way to Indochina. At least one former POW had committed suicide shortly after he returned home.

Who should go on the wall? The VVMF could only rely on the Department of Defense: If the Pentagon, acting in accordance with presidential directives specifying Vietnam, Laos, Cambodia, and coastal areas as combat zones, listed an individual as a fatality or as missing in action, his name would be included. Heartbreak notwithstanding, nothing could be done about the rest.

The names were also at the center of a dispute between Maya Lin and the vets. Her design called for names to be listed in the order of the day they died. She argued that this was essential to her design. The wall, she said, would read like an epic Greek poem. Vets could find their story told, and their friends remembered, in the panel that corresponded to their tour of duty. Locating specific names, with the aid of a directory, would be like finding bodies on a battlefield.

Some vets initially disagreed. If nearly 60,000 names were scattered along the wall, anyone looking for a specific name would wander around for hours and leave in frustration. One solution seemed obvious: List everyone in alphabetical order.

But when the vets examined a two-inch-thick Defense Department listing of Vietnam fatalities, their thinking changed. There were over 600 Smiths; 16 people named James Jones had died in Vietnam. Alphabetical listing would make the memorial look like a telephone book engraved in granite, destroying the sense of profound, unique loss each name carried.

The vets admitted Maya Lin was right.

▲   ▲   ▲

On September 20, 1982, sculptor Frederick Hart pulled back a tarpaulin covering a 14-inch-high model of his statue. "One senses the figures as passing by the tree line and, caught in the presence of the wall, turning to gaze upon it almost as a vision," he told

reporters. "There is about them the physical contact and sense of unity that bespeaks the bonds of love and sacrifice that is the nature of men at war. And yet they are each alone."

To the vets, the statue looked true. Boonie hat.[2] Facial expressions. Fatigues. Helmet. Dog tags[3] in a boot. Way of holding weapons. The men were strong, yet vulnerable. Committed, yet confused. Wheeler told reporters that the sons and daughters of men killed in Vietnam would look at the statue and say, "This is my father I never saw him alive. But he wore those clothes. He carried that weapon. He was young. I see now, and know him better."

As construction of the wall was rushed to meet the deadline set by the upcoming Veterans Day weekend ceremonies, many people simply stood outside the eight-foot construction fence waiting for a glimpse. Construction workers usually let family members and vets inside. An older man found his son's name, and stood there, clear-eyed and staring. But when he recognized nearby names, people his son had mentioned in letters, the man started to sob.

Most people did something unexpected. They touched the stone. Even young children reached up to fathers and uncles they had never known. The touches were gentle, filled with feeling, as if the stone were alive.

A Navy pilot in uniform brought with him a Purple Heart. "It belonged

2 **Boonie hat:** canvas, camouflage hat used to protect soldiers from the sun

3 **Dog tags:** metal identification tags containing name, unit, and serial number often worn like a necklace around a soldier's neck

to my brother," he explained. "He and I flew together. I'd like to put it with the concrete that's being poured."

The pilot saluted as the medal disappeared into the wall.

October brought government approval of the statue, as vets and their families from all over the country began streaming into Washington for dedication of the memorial. One vet walked 3,000 miles. Another sold his household appliances for airfare. Groups checked out of VA hospitals. And in the Midwest a couple heard about the upcoming ceremony on TV, finished dinner, cleared the table, got in the car, and started driving.

"It was," reported a newspaper in Beaumont, Texas, "as if they were all drawn by the same ghostly bugle."

For weeks, volunteers had been practicing reading names for a 56-hour vigil during which every name on the wall would be read in a chapel at the National Cathedral in Washington.

The hardest part was preparing not to cry. Pronunciation was also a problem and a Polish priest, a Spanish teacher, and a rabbi supplied expert advice.

"Rhythmic Spanish names. Tongue-twisting Polish names, guttural German, exotic African, homely Anglo-Saxon names," wrote *Newsweek* editor-in-chief William Broyles, Jr., who served in Vietnam as a Marine infantry lieutenant. "The war was about names, each name a special human being who never came home."

When you lost a son in Vietnam, you did everything you could to never forget anything about him. You made yourself remember conversations and scenes over and over again. You studied family photographs. You climbed to the attic and opened the cedar chest in which he'd stored his things. You touched the American flag that had come home with him.

So much had been taken from you, so you clung to the one thing they could never take away, something that had been with you since the joy of his birth: his name.

The names were read in alphabetical order, from Gerald L. Aadland of Sisseton, South Dakota, to David L. Zywicke of Manitowoc, Wisconsin.

Each name was like a bell tolling. As it was read aloud in the chapel, each ripped into the heart, into old wounds that could heal only after they had been reopened.

Time slots when names would be read were announced, so their sound could reach across America to people who loved them.

In Oklahoma, for example, at the exact moment her son's name was being said out loud, a woman stopped feeding her chickens and whispered a prayer.

A Congressional Medal of Honor winner who had volunteered to read names lasted five minutes before he broke down. He read the rest of the names on his knees.

▲　▲　▲

With more than 150,000 people in town for the dedication, Washington's hotels, restaurants, and streets filled with vets. It was, said one happy ex-GI, "one helluva party."

After many beers, a vet said he had won the Medal of Honor but was afraid of how people would react. To the cheers of a crowded bar, he opened his suitcase, took out the medal with its blue ribbon, and put it on for the first time. A man in a wheelchair slowly pushed through another bar that was filled to capacity. At first no one noticed him. Slowly, the noise faded, and then people reached out to touch him. A former medic sat in a corner, crying. He pushed away all who tried to console him. "I should have saved more," he kept saying. "I should have saved more."

Another ex-medic was walking down the sidewalk when a man grabbed him.

"You remember me?" the man said.

"No," the medic replied.

"Well, I was shot up pretty bad. Take a close look."

"Sorry, brother, I still don't know you."

"Well, I remember *you*, man. You saved my ass. Thanks."

▲　▲　▲

The vets, along with the American public, discovered the wall.

At night, they used matches, cigarette lighters, and torches made from rolled newspapers to find names. Volunteers stayed until dawn passing out flashlights. One father struck match after match, and then said to his wife, in a hushed voice, "There's Billy."

On Saturday, November 13, Vietnam vets marched down Constitution Avenue to the memorial in one of the largest processions the nation's capital had seen since John F. Kennedy's funeral.

Following speeches by dignitaries, the crowd sang "God Bless America," and paused for a moment of silence. "Ladies and gentlemen," Jan Scruggs said, "the Vietnam Veterans Memorial is now dedicated."

The tightly packed mass surged forward, crushing fences erected for crowd control. As thousands of hands strained to touch names, a lone GI climbed to the top of the wall, put a bugle to his lips and played taps, slowly. Between each note people seemed frozen, stunned by emotion. Nearby, another vet thrust a sign into the ground. "Honor the dead, fight like hell for the living," it said.

All afternoon, all night, the next day and the next and the next for an unbroken stream of months and years, millions of Americans have come and experienced that frozen moment.

The names have a power, a life, all their own. Even on the coldest days, sunlight makes them warm to the touch. Young men put into the earth, rising out of the earth. You can feel their blood flowing again.

Everyone, including those who knew no one who served in Vietnam, seems to touch the stone. Lips say a name over and over, and then stretch up to kiss it. Fingertips trace letters.

Perhaps by touching, people renew their faith in love and in life; or perhaps they better understand sacrifice and sorrow

"We're with you," they say. "We will never forget." ॐ

Responding to Cluster Four

Thinking Skill SYNTHESIZING

1. Each of the other clusters in this book is introduced by a question that is meant to help readers focus their thinking about the selections. What do you think the question for cluster four should be?

2. How do you think the selections in this cluster should be taught? Demonstrate your ideas by joining with your classmates to

   a) create discussion questions.
   b) lead discussions about the selections.
   c) develop vocabulary quizzes.
   d) prepare a cluster quiz.

Reflecting on *Times of Change: Vietnam and the 60s*

Essential Question WHAT EFFECT DID THE DECADE OF THE 60s HAVE ON THE UNITED STATES?

Reflecting on this book as a whole provides an opportunity for independent learning and the application of the critical thinking skill, synthesis. *Synthesizing* means examining all the things you have learned from this book and combining them to form a richer and more meaningful view of the era of the Vietnam War and the 1960s.

There are many ways to demonstrate what you know about the Vietnam War and the 60s. Here are some possibilities. Your teacher may provide others.

1. In "A Piece of My Heart" Ann Simon Auger says she "built up walls" to cope with the horrors she witnessed in Vietnam. Using the information in this book and what you might discover from other sources, discuss in an essay or speech why "walls" might be necessary.

2. Individually or in small groups, develop an independent project that demonstrates your knowledge of America during the 60s. For example, you might create your own documentary video. Other options might include a music video, dance, poem, performance, drama, or artistic rendering.

Acknowledgments

Text Credits continued from page 2   "I-Feel-Like-I'm-Fixin-To-Die Rag" by Country Joe McDonald. Copyright © Joe McDonald, BMI, 1965 renewed 1993 by Alkatraz Corner Music, BMI.

"Hippies" from *Camelot to Kent State* by Joan Morrison and Robert K. Morrison. Copyright © 1987 by Joan Morrison and Robert K. Morrison. Currently available in paperback from Times Books. Reprinted by permission of John A. Ware Literary Agency.

"Village" by Estela Portillo Trambley

"Farmer Nguyen" reprinted from *To Those Who Have Gone Home Tired*, W. D. Ehrhart (New York: Thunder's Mouth Press, 1984) by permission of the author.

"The Massacre at My Lai" by Hugh Thompson as appeared in *Newsweek*, March 8, 1999. Reprinted by permission of the author.

"A Nun in Ninh Hoa" by Jan Barry from *Carrying the Darkness*, Ehrhart, W. D.. Lubbock, TX: Texas Tech University Press, 1985. Reprinted by permission of the author.

Reprinted with permission from: *A Piece of my Heart*, Keith Walker © 1985 Presidio Press, Novato, CA.

San Francisco (Be Sure to Wear Flowers in Your Hair) Words and Music by John Phillips. © Copyright 1967, 1995 Universal - MCA Music Publishing, Inc., a division of Universal Studios, Inc. (ASCAP) Copyright Renewed. International Copyright Secured. All Rights Reserved.

"Law and Order Chicago Style" from *How To Light A Water Heater And Other War Stories: A Random Collection Of Random Essays*, by Donald Kaul. Copyright © 1970 The Iowa State University Press. Reprinted by permission.

From *The Rice Room: Growing Up Chinese-American from Number Two Son to Rock 'N' Roll* by Ben Fong-Torres. Copyright © 1994 by Ben Fong-Torres. Reprinted by permission of Hyperion.

From *Art Attack* by Marc Aronson. Text copyright © 1998 by Marc Aronson. Reprinted by permission of Clarion Books/Houghton Mifflin Company. All rights reserved.

Reprinted with permission from "Woodstock:The Oral History", by Joel Makower. Copyright © 1989 by Tilden Press, Inc.

"State Of Emergency At 'The People's Republic Of Berkeley'" from *Reunion: A Memoir* by Tom Hayden. Reprinted by permission of Senator Tom Hayden, Democrat, Los Angeles.

"The Kent State Tragedy" from *The Vietnam War* by Roger Barr. Copyright 1991 by Lucent Books. Reprinted by permission.

From *Born on the Fourth of July* by Ron Kovic. Copyright © 1976 by Ron Kovic. Reprinted by permission of The McGraw-Hill Companies.

Where Have All The Flowers Gone by Pete Seeger. Copyright © 1961 (renewed) by Sanga Music, Inc. All Rights Reserved. Used by permission.

From: *A Rumor of War* by Philip Caputo, © 1977 by Philip Caputo. Reprinted by permission of Henry Holt and Company, LLC.

"A President's Pain as We Sound Retreat" by Gerald R. Ford as appeared in *Newsweek*, March 8, 1999. Reprinted by permission of the Honorable Gerald R. Ford.

"The Summer of Vietnam" by Barbara Renaud Gonzalez. Copyright © 1992 by Barbara Renaud Gonzalez. First published in *New Chicana/Chicano Writing*, University of Arizonia Press. Reprinted by permission of Susan Bergholz Literary Services, New York. All rights reserved.

"Stop The Sun" by Gary Paulson. First appeared in *Boy's Life Magazine*, January 1986. Copyright © 1986 by Gary Paulson. Reprinted by permission.

"To Heal A Nation" from *The Field: A Collection of Writings From National Geographic*, by Joel Swerdlow. Copyright © 1997 National Geographic Society. Reprinted by permission.

Every reasonable effort has been made to properly acknowledge ownership of all material used. Any omissions or mistakes are not intentional and, if brought to the publisher's attention, will be corrected in future editions.

PHOTO AND ART CREDITS Cover (Detail), Back Cover and Title Page (Complete): Kenneth Willhite, *The Vietnam War,* 1984. Watercolor and gouache on board, 30 x 20 inches. Courtesy The National Vietnam Veterans Art Museum, Chicago. Page 3: Henri Huet, AP/Wide World Photos. Pages 4-5: ©2000 Nacio Jan Brown/Black Star. Page 9: L, © Bettmann/Corbis; TR, FPG International; BR, NASA. Page 10: L. L. Darr/FPG International; Inset, © Bettmann/Corbis. Pages 12-13: T, Robert Altman; B, FPG International. Page 15: U.S. Marine Corps/National Archives. Pages 16-17: T, © Andi Martin/Photonica; B, USAF/National Archives. Page 17: U.S. Department of Defense/National Archives. Pages 18-19: National Archives. Page 20: Frank Wolfe/LBJ Library. Pages 20-21: U.S. Navy/National Archives. Page 22: Charlie Shobe, *On the Road to Con Thien,* 1980. Oil on canvas, 24 x 18 inches. Courtesy The National Vietnam Veterans Art Museum, Chicago. Page 30: Charlie Shobe, *Class of '67,* 1984. Oil on canvas, ca. 22 x 28 inches. Courtesy The National Vietnam Veterans Art Museum, Chicago. Page 32: Glenn Priestley, *Bellamy 9,* 1988. Page 39: Douglas Brega, *Emerson,* 1986. Page 47: Ken Moylan, *Boundary Lake,* 1995. Courtesy Thomas Barry Fine Arts, Minneapolis. Page 49: Huynh Cong 'Nick' Ut/AP/Wide World. Pages 50-51: Art Greenspon/AP/Wide World. Page 52: Herb Greene, courtesy Walnut Street Gallery. Page 54: AP/Wide World. Page 56: P. G. Griffiths/Magnum Photos, Inc. Pages 56-57, 64-65: Steve Raymer/NGS Image Collection. Page 65: Sp. 4. John Olson, U.S. Army/ National Archives, (127-N-A185146). Page 66: Ron Haeberle/Life/Timepix. Page 69: Kamil Vojnar/Photonica. Page 70: Anne Simon Auger from *A Piece of My Heart* by Keith Walker, Presidio Press, 1985. Page 74: Mark Jury. Page 79: Robert Altman. Pages 80-81: ©Tom Miner/The Image Works; S. I. Yamamoto/Photonica. Page 83: UPI/Corbis-Bettmann. Page 85: Barry Olivier. Page 88: ©1989 Charles Harbutt/Actuality Inc.; John Dominis/Life/Timepix. Page 90: TL, © Henry Diltz/Corbis; BR, © Lauren Radack/Corbis. Page 91: Arnold Skolnick, Woodstock, *3 Days of Peace and Music–and Love.* Offset lithograph. Poster. New York, 1969. National Archives (LC-USZC4-19111, LC-USZ62-96354), © 1970 Warner Bros., Inc. Pages 94-95: AP/Wide World. Page 98: © Corbis. Pages 100-101: Akron Beacon Journal. Page 102: John Filo. Page 105: Jeffrey Sylvester/FPG International. Page 107: © Neal Preston/Corbis. Page 108: Bernie Boston. Page 111: © Fernando & Mercedes/ Corbis. Page 115: © Bettmann/Corbis. Page 118: Gilles Caron/Contact Press Images, Inc. Page 120: Ned Broderick, *Hi Mom...I'm Home,* 1994. Oil on hardboard, 30 x 30 inches. Courtesy The National Vietnam Veterans Art Museum, Chicago. Page 128: Christopher Morris/Black Star. Pages 128-129: Susan Meiselas/ Magnum Photos, Inc. Page 137: Michael Katakis from *The Vietnam Veterans Memorial* by Michael Katakis, Crown Publishers (Random House, Inc.), 1988. Page 138: J. Scott Applewhite/AP/Wide World. Pages 140-141: Everett C. Johnson/Folio Inc.